John Castell was born just before World War II, in 1937. He was brought up in the countryside, and developed a love of animals and enjoyed riding horses. He became committed to belief in God when about 12 years old and that has strengthened as the years go by. He attended a very good Grammar School and after that, the University of London. As a post-graduate he obtained a Ph.D in the Faculty of Medicine. He had an interesting career in medical microbiology. He was head of a large department of scientists and sat on some international committees.

John Castell

HUMANS EVOLVED, PEOPLE WERE MADE

AUSTIN MACAULEY PUBLISHERS™

LONDON * CAMBRIDGE * NEW YORK * SHARJAH

A CIP catalogue record for this title is available from the British Library.

ISBN 9781035800292 (Paperback)
ISBN 9781035800308 (Hardback)
ISBN 9781035800315 (ePub e-book)

www.austinmacauley.com

First Published 2023
Austin Macauley Publishers Ltd®
1 Canada Square
Canary Wharf
London
E14 5AA

Table of Contents

Preface

I decided to write this book because I wanted to help people who believe in God not to be dismayed by what atheists say about science and to give believers a better understanding of the true relationship between science and theology.

This is not a book for atheists. A committed atheist who denies the existence of God, the soul and a spiritual world will disagree with most of this book. It was not written to try to influence atheists, a task that I feel unequal to, but rather to support believers with fair and truthful information about people and evolution. To help believers in God not to be worried by what unbelievers say about science.

In this book, we consider some important topics surrounding the concepts of God, evolution and people: to uphold the integrity of science and the integrity of theology and to try to help understanding of the relationship between these subjects and our knowledge of the spiritual and physical worlds. There is only one God. There is a physical world and a spiritual world. People are a combination of a physical body and a spiritual soul. Because of this it is impossible for evolution to explain the existence of people: evolution deals only with baryonic matter but the first defining characteristic of people, which separates us clearly from all other life, is the soul. Evolution could not have introduced a soul, only God could have done that. The second defining characteristic is our wonderfully complex language, which is unique to people and is also a gift from God.

For many years, there have been some people who do not believe in God, although all people are capable of understanding the concept of a God and the great majority of people are believers in God. For believers, worship of God is a duty, an inspiration and a source of strength. Each individual person has to come to this important decision for themselves and many influences bear upon the outcome, especially the minds of their parents, teachers and friends. Recent years have seen the appearance of militant atheists, who argue strenuously against belief in God and try to recruit people to their view. Since most religious organisations also try to convert people to their belief, it is not unreasonable for atheists to do this, providing that the arguments they use are fair and appropriate. In many cases they are not, because atheists often use scientific arguments to support their views. This is wrong because atheism is not a branch of science: it is a branch of religion. Science and theology (religion) are completely different disciplines and science cannot be used to debate religion. Those who wish to argue against the existence of a God can only do this respectably by using theological arguments, not scientific ones.

This book is about science, theology and religion, but the word "religion" now has many negative associations in the minds of some people, for example the cruelty of some religious sects to people of a different sect, and the idea that religion is used to control people and may contribute to sexual inequality. Theology is the study of God. Religion is the application of theology in lifetime situations. When reading this book, it is hoped that the word "religion" will not be taken to refer specifically to existing "Religions", but rather to the general concept of people believing in God. Science should not be used to argue against belief in God because there is no conflict between science and religion. Science was created by God at the outset. God does not usually interfere with the laws that he has made.

In this book, the word "God" is intended to mean the monotheistic God of the Abrahamic religions: The one creator God of the Israelites, Christians and Muslims and anyone else who believes in this one God.

The word "people" is used in this book to mean present day people, and people like us who have lived in the historical period, and for some unknown length of time before that. You and I are people: we are clearly distinguishable from the "humans" who came before us, who were the result of millions of years of development from earlier forms.

Evolution is a word that describes the increasing complexity of the plant and animal kingdoms, over millions of years, from single cell beginnings to the diversity seen today. A scientific definition of biological evolution is that evolution is a process that results in changes in the genetic material of a population over time. This biological evolution produced the hominid line, culminating in *Homo sapiens*, but it did not produce the people we are now, who arose in the last 70,000 years. We are a sub-species, or variety of *H. sapiens*, as proposed by Carl von Linne, known as Linnaeus (1707–1778) who invented the binomial system of naming plants and animals. He said that we are distinct from the earlier form and we should be named *Homo sapiens var. sapiens.*

It is important to understand, at the outset, the difference between "evolution" and "Natural Selection". It is often said that Charles Darwin proposed a theory of evolution but in fact what he proposed was the theory of Natural Selection. The idea of development of species from pre-existing forms had been proposed by others before him, notably Robert Chambers in his book "Vestiges of Natural Creation", published 15 years before Darwin published "On the origin of species". What Darwin proposed was the theory of Natural Selection, which is supposed to explain how evolution actually works. But Darwin himself believed that the inheritance of acquired characteristics was very important to support his theory, and we now know that this does not happen (except for possible epigenetic effects). So although evolution might be regarded as not just a theory, but a theorem, as proposed by Richard Dawkins, Natural Selection, which was Darwin's (and Wallace's) contribution, cannot be considered as more than a theory, because it is not entirely clear how it works or how important it is. Natural Selection seems to be a reasonable explanation for much of micro-evolution, but in the absence of the inheritance of acquired characteristics, and given the paucity of *de novo* germ-line mutations, and given that these are usually harmful and recessive, it is not clear how enough useful variation came into existence, sufficient to support the large, macro-evolutionary changes that have evidently taken place. Recent increases in the understanding of genetics and genomics have reduced the importance given to Natural Selection in present day evolutionary theory.

Believers in God need have no difficulty with any of this. God made everything, including the natural laws that came into effect from the beginning. God made a living system that he loved and developed over a long period of time and ultimately he changed *Homo sapiens* into people. People who refuse to believe in a non-material world cannot accept this, but that does not make it any less true. This view will be fully supported later in the book. In brief, God revealed himself to people over many millennia, in ways appropriate to the times. Firstly to religious writers and later also to scientists. These two strands need to be viewed together so that a coherent account can be made of the development of the natural world and of people which is consistent with Divine revelation;

both spiritual revelation and revelation as seen in the material record and scientific inquiry.

All the Abrahamic religions, and others, believe that a person has an animal body and linked to it a spiritual entity, the soul. This soul is the true representation of the person; their real individual feelings, beliefs, attitudes and priorities. It is part of the spiritual world, not made of baryonic matter, and therefore not detectable by any scientific methods.

The Christian Church has had a long and uneasy feeling towards Darwin and Natural Selection. First, shocked and horrified, latterly feeling that it could not go against science and consequently somewhat disturbed. There is no need for anyone to be disturbed. The Church can accept the science of the development of hominids from earlier forms, up to the point of *H. sapiens.* But the Church (the Church in the broadest sense, that is, all believers in One God) knowing that people are not only a material body must also know that science cannot explain the sudden appearance of people with a soul. This is only explicable in the words of Genesis. God made man in his own image and likeness. Nothing else is possible, scientifically speaking. Only God can work with the world of the spirit. Only God could give people a soul. This must be the stance of the Church. To deny this, and say that people could have arisen through unaided evolution is to deny that a person has an everlasting, spiritual soul. The simple message of this book is that humans arose through a process of evolution over millions of years but that present day people are the result of a quite recent intervention by God, who gave the ancient hunter-gatherers a soul, language, intellect and immortality.

God did this to make one creature living on Earth who could talk to him.

That is why we exist: to talk to God.

Introduction

When Jesus Christ was alive on earth, there was hardly any knowledge that could be described as scientific in the way in which the word is used today. There was a lot of practical knowledge of the physical world, for example the description of agriculture given earlier by Virgil in the *Georgics,* and there was much practical knowledge about ceramics, metallurgy and engineering, but the scientific method had not been formalised. Most "scientific" knowledge, until a few centuries ago was based on the words of Aristotle. His influence was so great that his ideas were unchallenged until quite recent times, even though his ideas were far from what is known to be true through science today.

The last few centuries have seen an increasing accumulation of scientific knowledge about the physical world in which we live. The rate of increase of knowledge has itself increased exponentially. It is astonishing how little was known scientifically as recently as the mid-nineteenth century, compared with today. The past fifty years have probably seen greater advances than throughout all the preceding years. During all this time, the three great mono-theistic religions, the Jewish, Christian and Islamic, have continued essentially unchanged, as they have to. None of the five Great Universal Prophets; Abraham, Noah, Moses, Jesus and Muhammad needed to say anything about science, because it was not actively studied in their times.

Unfortunately this development of knowledge about the physical world has led to some recent conflict between science and religion. When some atheist scientists of Darwin's day, notably Thomas Henry Huxley, heard about Natural Selection, they tried to use it in support of their wish to make a complete separation of science from religion, that is to separate the physical world from the spiritual world, which they did not believe in. That wish to separate the two was good up to a point, but they went too far. They said there was only science, only a physical world. They said that Natural Selection explained all the diversity of life, without any need for a Creator, but refused to admit that this did not rule out a Creator. Of course they did not fully comprehend Natural Selection, either, and had no knowledge of cytology and genetics. They just wished to destroy the idea of a non-material world. This was not logical because science can only detect things that are within its own area of competence: that is the material world. The existence of a non-material, spiritual world can never be disproved by science. It is impossible to prove that something does not exist.

Since that time some people have developed a world-view which denies the existence of a non-material world and hence denies the existence of God. This unbalanced focus on the material world, to the exclusion of the non-material world, has led to the emergence of atheists who turn to science for support of their views. This in turn has led to some damage to the integrity of science. Even without that, there is a lot of misrepresentation associated with science and the way it is reported; too much importance attached to trivial or not fully substantiated work; premature over-celebration of work which might prove useful in decades to come; presenting results in a misleading way: reporting something as science when it is not science; a tendency to regard humans as no different from animals.

Religion is not free from distortion either, and it is very regrettable that in recent times some secular governments are interfering with religious beliefs, traditions and moral standards. Theology is also subject to distorted interpretations when some exegetes allow their judgment to be clouded by liberal or other inappropriate influences. In this book we are discussing both theology and religion. Religion really refers to the many ways in which people respond to theological ideas. To get to the point, what we are talking about here is belief in God; belief in a non-material world. So when reading this book, do not think of "religion" in terms of existing world religions, but rather see the word as simply indicating a belief in God. Rather than a non-material world, it might be more appropriate for us to talk and think about an "other-material world". The world of the spirit must be made of something. Julian Huxley, the distinguished biologist and well-known atheist/agnostic recognised that mind and matter were different. He said that matter cannot occupy a space already occupied by other matter, but two minds can interpenetrate each other, which is true and happens continually. Because religion is really just the interpretation that *people* put on theology, it is better to leave out consideration of religion and keep to the subject of theology, which is the study of God.

It is argued here that there is no connection between the disciplines of theology and science. They are two completely separate intellectual processes, with no shared methodology. As such there can be no conflict between them, and efforts by atheists to weaken religion through the use of science are mischievous. They bring discredit to the proponents themselves and more importantly discredit the scientific method. Because of widespread lack of knowledge of what science really is, some of the assertions of atheists may be disconcerting to theists (believers). In my view, it is also incorrect to try to build bridges between science and theology. Rather, they should both be used to look at the same question, from different angles. (That was probably the belief of Charles Darwin.) Science is concerned only with the material world, whereas religion is concerned with the spiritual world, while taking note of the material world. Science cannot detect or recognise the spiritual world but that does not in any way detract from the importance of either.

Science has no instruments or methods for detecting the spiritual world, but people can detect it, because we are spirits, so we are already part of the spiritual world, although probably only incompletely while our physical bodies are alive. Although the working methods of scientists and theologians are distinct and different, some of the philosophical concepts which support science and theology are similar, leading to the development of what is called theological science, in recent decades.

Science itself at present has much uncertainty, especially regarding cosmology and particle physics. The material world that we are part of (made of baryonic matter) makes up only 4.9% of the total mass/energy of the universe. This book sets out to try, in some measure, to counter the harmful effects which can arise when the clear distinction between the disciplines of science and theology is not recognised. There is no conflict between science and theology: both of these subjects are valid and complementary methods for looking at the material and spiritual worlds we live in, respectively.

It is for each individual to decide whether or not they believe in God, but it is tragic if people come to this vitally important decision based on wrong information. There is nothing in the corpus of scientific knowledge, or in the application of the scientific method, which can have any meaningful influence on belief or disbelief in God, because God is a spirit and those who worship him must do so in spirit. Worship of God is the first duty of all people, an inspiration and a source of strength. It is a wholly spiritual activity, not affected in any way by scientific knowledge.

Some people think that the physical world can be explained without the need for God, but that does not mean that it *was* made without God. But only God could have made the spiritual world, which is our more important home. Only God could have made people, by giving us a soul, and the language, intellect and immortality that go with it.

This book is not in opposition to science, on the contrary it wishes to uphold the integrity of science. But it is necessary to demonstrate some deficiencies in recent scientific work, which have been used to argue against the existence of God. For example, there is increasing awareness that Charles Darwin's theory of Natural Selection, valuable though it is, has been given exaggerated importance by some people. It is being reviewed all the time as the Evolutionary Synthesis develops. It is important that claims are not made for scientific understanding that go further than what is very well established with a high level of probability. Of course there are still gaps in scientific knowledge which may take many years to be resolved, if ever. As a generalisation, science explains how things work without explaining why they are there. Theology can offer some insight into the question of purpose, especially in relation to the development of people from animal ancestors, in parallel with what evidence can be found in the material record. Science cannot answer the question: why are there people? This question has to be answered by reference to the world of the mind and spirit.

The scientific explanation for the creation of matter is, at present, the theory known informally as the Big Bang, or more correctly as the Concordance on the Lambda-CDM model, also referred to as the Standard Model of Cosmology, which was agreed by cosmologists in the late 1990s but is still controversial. [Lambda is the Greek letter used to signify the Cosmological Constant which is associated with vacuum energy. CDM stands for Cold Dark Matter.] The Standard Model is based on the assumption that General Relativity is the correct explanation for gravity. This theory has replaced the earlier theory, supported by Fred Hoyle and others in the 1950s, that matter had always existed as a diffuse "fog" that was everywhere and from which stars condensed, with continuous creation of new matter: the Steady State theory. This theory became untenable when the cosmic microwave background radiation throughout the universe was discovered. It was also incompatible with the second law of thermodynamics which states that entropy is always increasing (meaning that energy is being continuously used up). As the universe is constantly losing energy it cannot be everlasting. The realisation that the universe did have a finite starting point was of great philosophical importance. Only the world of the spirit is everlasting.

The Big Bang supposes that the origin of the universe was the sudden expansion of an initial energy that spread rapidly outwards. A lot happened in a very, very short time. Authoritative statements are made about the events of the first second but are subject to review and disagreement. The early events are largely speculative and it may be some time before theoretical physics can be more certain about this. The lambda-CDM theory supposes several Epochs. The first is the Planck Epoch, which lasted from 0 to 10^{-43} seconds. Very little is known about this time, but it is supposed that the four fundamental forces: electromagnetism, the strong nuclear force, the weak nuclear force and the force of gravity were present and possibly combined into one unified force. At that time, the universe was thought to be very small, extending only 10^{-35} metres. (About a billion, billion, billion, billionth of a metre). It was very hot, having a temperature of over 10^{32}°C. Later in the Inflationary Epoch, from 10^{-36} to 10^{-32} seconds the universe expanded rapidly in this tiny fraction of a second, by a factor of at least 10^{26}, growing in size to a linear dimension of ten centimetres. There are some cosmologists who say that the expansion was amazingly greater, increasing in size by a factor of 10^{50} which would mean that the universe expanded to 18 billion light years in that tiny amount of time.

The Big Bang itself, known to cosmologists as the "initial singularity", is not understood. It is not possible to imagine such short periods of intense activity together with such extreme temperatures. Do the mathematicians who do the sums ever stop to consider the feasibility of their results? Astrophysicists at The Laser Interferometer Gravitational-Wave Observatory (LIGO) announced their detection of inflationary gravitational waves at a press conference in February 2016. If their finding is confirmed it would provide experimental evidence supporting the theory which predicts this much greater inflation. However, researchers at the Niels Bohr Institute in Copenhagen are doubtful that the results have been fully separated from background noise, and therefore the results may not be valid. There are very great technical difficulties in detecting gravitational waves and it may be some time before this question is resolved.

The Lambda-CDM model, although it may have some inconsistencies, is generally accepted as the best fit theory at present. It accounts for the cosmic microwave background, the large-scale structure of the universe, the abundance of hydrogen, helium and lithium and for the accelerating expanding universe. But there are problems which it struggles to account for, such as the "flat universe". More details of the Lambda-CDM theory are given in the chapter *Science and Theology*. The purpose of discussing this is to highlight the fact that science does not currently have the answer to everything; there remains a lot of uncertainty.

What the Big Bang theory does do is to state that the Universe had a definite time of origin, calculated (2013) to be 13.798 billion years ago (plus or minus 37 million years), not as thought previously that it had always been there. This is very significant because perhaps the most important general principle of science is *cause and effect.* Every event must have a cause, expressed neatly in Latin as *Ex nihilo nihil fit* [out of nothing, nothing comes]. But the Big Bang does demand some originating cause. There is no agreed scientific explanation so far, for how it happened. What caused it to happen? For what reason did it happen? Only God knows the answers to these questions.

Also, we see that the material world will have an end. The Second Law of Thermodynamics indicates that the Universe is winding down, energy is lost and entropy increases. So the material world that we live in and are a part of had a very sudden beginning, a very long time ago, it is passing through a very long phase of development from simple to more complex forms, and it will have a slow and gradual ending, a very, very long time in the future. In contrast to this, it is believed that the non-material world of the spirit does not decay: it is everlasting. It is believed that God has always existed and will always exist.

From the initial event, the laws of physics were apparent and caused the sequence of events that led to the production of a range of atoms of different sizes, stars and planets. Planet Earth is calculated to be about 4.54 billion years old. Various theories seek to explain the creation of the Earth and the vast quantity of water on the Earth. It is thought that life began on Earth about half a billion years after the planet formed. How this happened is not known although there are many theories. Life began as a very simple, single cell structure, and remained that way for billions of years, until single cell organisms began to join up to form multicellular organisms. Life really began to diversify in the last half billion years. By 100 million years ago, there was a flourishing fauna and flora: the dinosaurs and the ferns were doing well. Further diversification has taken place since then, with new species emerging and some old ones dying out. The Darwin-Wallace theory of evolution explains this by a process of Natural

Selection. Darwin thought that this could explain all life, including present day people, but Wallace thought that it could explain life up to the appearance of *H. sapiens*, but not the appearance of people like us. In this book, a case is made that Wallace was correct.

The theory of Natural Selection, as proposed by Charles Darwin and Alfred Russell Wallace, was combined with studies from population genetics to form the "Modern Evolutionary Synthesis", which was developed by Julian Huxley and others in the 1930s. This provides a widely accepted explanation for the diversity of animal and plant life that has developed on planet Earth, but there appear to be some uncertainties and deficiencies in the theory that are still unresolved. The Modern Evolutionary Synthesis requires further analysis, and is itself under review by present day scientists.

Natural selection and "survival of the fittest" are intuitively understandable as influences that will tend to develop species that are increasingly well adapted to their environment: improvement in response to need. But it should be noted that if a designer was responsible for the gradual improvement of species over time, the appearance given would be just the same as Natural Selection and survival of the fittest, because a designer tests their new designs against a yardstick of efficiency in any particular application and milieu, and rejects the less suitable. It would look the same, either way. Only people who deny the existence of a designer deny the existence of design in the universe.

Influences which bring about change have been working on the higher mammals for a long time. About seven million years ago the primate lineage developed a branch that was characterised by bipedalism, which led to the several hominid species described so far, and by about 150,000 years ago to the emergence of *Homo sapiens*.

Although present day people are classified by biologists as *Homo sapiens*, we are very different from the *H. sapiens* of 150 thousand or more years ago, mainly because of our mental and behavioural characteristics. Linnaeus recognised this, calling modern people *Homo sapiens, var. sapiens*. But many present-day writers appear to think that there is no difference at all between us and the *H. sapiens* of 100,000 years ago: that is nonsense. Suppose that one could take a man from 5,000 years ago, teach him to speak English, teach him acceptable rules of social conduct and take him to a good tailor, it would then be possible to take him to lunch at an exclusive Gentleman's Club, and nobody would see anything unusual about him. But if the same was attempted with a man from 100,000 years ago, it would probably prove impractical, but if it was done it is very likely that he would immediately be seen to be very unusual. He would not fit in. The essential difference between the 100,000 years ago man who failed the test and the 5,000 years ago man who passed the test is that the latter was a *person* (like us) but the former was not.

Present day people have minds that are essentially the same as people five or six thousand years ago. This is evident from the written record. Before there was writing, one can only speculate about the mental attributes of the more ancient humans. The most important of the differences between ourselves and the ancient humans is that present day people understand the concept of God and the concept of good and evil. It is unlikely that the humans of 100,000 years ago had that ability, because they almost certainly did not have the language to support sophisticated abstract concepts. Present day people possess very complex language which is amazingly complete in its ability to express all the subtleties of philosophical ideas, and people also have great curiosity and are immensely creative. None of these attributes and abilities have been developed in other life forms, except to a degree so rudimentary as to be comparatively insignificant.

This unique ability of people to understand the meaning of right and wrong will be considered further in a later chapter, but its importance needs emphasis here. When a cat plays with a sparrow, letting it flutter away and then pouncing on it again, killing it in slow stages, the cat feels no pity, remorse or shame. It is doing what its instinct tells it to do, improving its hunting skills without a thought for the feelings of the bird. This is true of all nature, it operates without conscience. But a person understands the meaning of right and wrong, not simplistically, but with an understanding of the principles that underlie these concepts. Some people might suggest that a dog understands the meaning of right and wrong. At a very simple level that can be true. A dog can be taught that to catch a rabbit is "good" but to chase a sheep is "bad". This is done by rewarding the dog when it catches a rabbit and punishing the dog when it chases a sheep. Such lessons are soon learnt, but the dog has no understanding of the principles on which judgement about right and wrong is made. The dog is reacting in the way that a child reacts when told not to touch the hot stove. The child disobeys, touches the stove and gets a sore finger from the hot surface. It learns that to touch the stove is therefore "bad", because they got hurt. But this is "bad" to them, because it resulted in harm to them. This event does not instil any understanding of conscience, which is concerned with harm to other people.

Avoiding harm to oneself is prudence, and the dog and child in these examples understood the concept of prudence: of self-preservation, which is the strongest of primitive instincts. But to understand the need to distinguish between actions that are helpful or harmful to *others,* and especially to understand the concept of good and evil: actions that are pleasing or displeasing to God, is immensely complex. It depends on having a *conscience* and requires an intellect that can use language to analyse abstract thought processes. It is therefore a unique attribute of people because only people have the qualities of *mind* and the very sophisticated language that are essential for this. Only people have a conscience to guide them. This conscience cannot be present in a very young child because it does not have the necessary language. The child is blameless like the animals. Robert Chambers, who will be discussed in later chapters, wrote clearly about this. His mid-nineteenth century words may seem harsh to a modern reader but are true. "In infancy, the impulses are all of them irregular; a child is cruel, cunning and false, under the slightest temptation, but in time learns to control these inclinations, and to be habitually humane, frank and truthful."

There has therefore been a sequence of development from "animal" to "person", but not in one step. The animal first developed into a human and the human then became a person. The first hominids to pick up a flint and make more flakes from it, and later make purposeful use of fire marked the point of departure from the essentially incurious and non-creative animals. These humans survived for a long time and have only recently been replaced by people. But "people" can also be seen to have developed in two stages. First there was the improvement of the human, to make the first people, who were able to talk to God, but knew only about "good", and lived in harmony with God and each other. The second stage was the introduction of the understanding of "evil". This event, known as The Fall, modified people so that they were no longer innocent: they had knowledge of good and evil. This led to disharmony with God, and led to violent conflict with each other.

Charles Darwin tried hard to show that his theory of Natural Selection applied across all living things, without any exception. His book "The Descent of Man" will be discussed in detail in one of the chapters that follow. Darwinian evolution does help to explain the development of the human but it is proposed here that it does not explain the recent development of people. Natural Selection and survival of the fittest are valid concepts for the early stages of human development, although there are many difficulties in understanding how Natural

Selection really worked. Recent advances in knowledge are tending to reduce the importance of Natural Selection as a force in evolution.

The scientific reason for the failure of Darwin's Natural Selection to explain the emergence of people is that the minds of people are better than we need. This statement will be expanded upon later in the book. It is true even nowadays that our minds are very much better than most of our activities require. The similar minds of the ancient hunter-gatherers were much better than they needed to be for their simple way of life. This was the idea that came to Darwin's contemporary Alfred Russell Wallace through his contact with the natives of the Amazon basin and the Malay Archipelago and led to his difference of opinion with Darwin on this subject. Our minds are not the result of need, and therefore not the result of Darwinian evolution, which is rooted in response to need. This was the initial impetus behind the writing of this book. It is the wonderful mind of people that distinguishes us from earlier humans and this mind did not result from Natural Selection because it was already much more efficient than the demands of life required. It was not simply due to having a larger brain, either, because we have brains with only about three times the processing power of other primates, who live very successful lives with minds that are vastly inferior to ours. They have had just as long as us to develop better intellects, but they did not do so, because it would not have been to their advantage in the life style they led. A gorilla does not need to know the mathematical relationship between the lengths of the sides of a right-angled triangle that were worked out by Pythagoras. Neither do we, most of the time.

But there is a deeper reason for knowing that people were not made by the unaided application of Natural Selection. This is because people are a combination of an animal body with a spiritual soul. Natural Selection is a purely physical process and therefore cannot have any influence on the soul. The first *Homo sapiens* did not have a soul. They had no language and no knowledge of good and evil. The soul was given them much later. Only God could have done that. The soul was not made by small incremental steps over a period of time. You either have one or you do not have one. So there was a moment when God "made man in his image" by giving him a soul. These were the first people, who had language and conscience. The Bible describes the creation of one man, Adam, and one woman, Eve, but it seems to me that this could be a simplification and that a group of humans were created together at the same time. Cain, who was the son of Adam and Eve, was able to marry "one of the daughters of men", so evidently there were humans living at the same time that Adam and Eve were created, and they could interbreed so they were the same species.

The massive development of the human intellect, far beyond the needs of our lives, is in contrast to the minds of other higher animals. Other animals, such as a wolf or a horse, have developed their intelligence until they have all they need to be very good at what they are: what they need to be and to do. Then their intellectual development stopped. All the higher animals have all the intelligence they need to be very good at what they are, and have remained on this plateau for a very long time. It may be possible to demonstrate some difference in intelligence between two individuals of the same species, but such differences are the fine tuning: the essential intelligence is there in them all. There are also many notable examples of innate knowledge, such as the spider knowing how to make its web without instruction, the beaver its dam and birds their nests. It is not clear how an idea can get into the genome.

People have had an "intelligence beyond immediate utility"—as Alfred Russell Wallace wrote—for a long time, but recently our behaviour took a great leap forward. History shows that five or six thousand years ago there were people who thought in exactly the same fashion as we do, as we see from their writing. Before the survival of written records, there is no certainty about how people thought, but the material record is quite clear that about 10,000 years ago there was a sudden change in behaviour of people from being hunter-gatherers, living a nomadic life in small family groups with few possessions and no social structure, to settled communities of people living in villages with more possessions, an emerging social structure and the development of agriculture, including the domestication of animals and plants.

The hunter-gatherer behaviour had continued for probably more than 60,000 years, then very suddenly changed about ten thousand years ago. This is what the Cambridge professor of archaeology, Lord Renfrew, has called "*The sapient paradox*". What caused this to happen? Clearly it was too recent and too sudden to be anything to do with genetic changes or any kind of evolution.

All people living today are thought by geneticists (on the basis of mitochondrial DNA) to be descended from three or four women, who lived about 65,000 years ago. At that time, the human population was, it is thought, reduced to a very small number of breeding pairs with a total population of between one and ten thousand. We are genetically almost identical to the humans of that time, but it is almost certain that they did not have the mental attributes that make us the *people* we are today.

It is proposed here that the answer to Lord Renfrew's *sapient paradox* is that the sudden change in behaviour that took place 10,000 years ago was brought about by fear. The hunter-gatherers had their fears, no doubt. They were in danger from wild animals and from natural disasters. But they did not fear each other. Like most other higher animals, they generally did not prey upon others of their own species. What changed was that they became fearful of each other.

The old *Homo sapiens* was similar to other animals, without a conscience, unable to recognise good or bad deeds and therefore not capable of sin. The Bible describes the creation of Adam and Eve who knew only good, until Eve disobeyed God in what is called the Fall. The Fall was essentially due to Eve wanting something that she was not supposed to have. The Bible suggests that The Fall took place very soon after the creation of Adam and Eve because they had no sexual intercourse until after The Fall. After that, Adam and Eve understood both good and evil. Their son Cain killed his own brother Abel, one of the worst things a person can do. He did this through envy for his brother, because the sacrifices of Abel were more pleasing to God than his own.

It is suggested here that people did not do much that was evil until a long time after that. This was because the hunter-gatherers led simple lives with very few possessions, so they did not see someone else with more possessions than they had themselves: there was no stimulus for evil; no temptation. The dog who does wrong in the eyes of its owner by chasing a sheep cannot do that if it does not see a sheep.

What probably happened was that some individuals began to acquire wealth, which led to inequality and others began to feel envy towards them, which is evil. Then some people began to attack others to take by force what they wanted. After that, people had to band together into villages for protection. From that arose the need for agriculture; to feed a more densely populated place. But it must be remembered that the defining difference between ourselves and the old *Homo sapiens* is that we have soul, language and conscience, and these are not physical characteristics. There are, of course, speech centres in the brain, but these are concerned with the production of speech. Language and conscience are spiritual, not physical. Perhaps they are passed on without any contact with the genome. The way God has interacted with mankind has always been through a spiritual rather than a physical activity.

God created the spiritual and physical worlds, including the Earth, and evolution was part of his creative method, but the evolution of man (in the Darwinian sense) stopped at the point of *Homo sapiens*. After that, God gave the human the God-like qualities of an immortal soul, creativity and love, the knowledge of good and the ability to speak God's language to each other and to him. This was a sudden, once only event. In physical terms, it can probably be partly explained by the installation of additional software into the brain, providing programmes for language, abstract thought, conscience and creativity.

The change from human to person must have happened just before the migration out of Africa, about 65,000 years ago, so that it applied to both those who remained in Africa and to those who left and peopled the rest of the world. It is thought that there were not many humans living at that time, probably fewer than ten thousand. People existed in the innocent form for only a short time before The Fall changed them to the people we are today with knowledge of good and evil. But although they knew both good and evil, they led essentially good and innocent lives for many thousands of years without temptation, until the sudden change to sedentism 10,000 years ago.

Those people were the hunter-gatherers, who spread widely, and lived essentially "good" lives, obeying the will of God. They lived in harmony with each other without envy because none of them had more than their most basic requirements. There was no wealth in the modern sense of the word. The material record shows that this simple nomadic life was maintained for about 60,000 years. Then there was the sudden change to sedentism. It is proposed here that this came about because improving climatic conditions led to less rigorous living, with the opportunity for leisure and acquisition of wealth. This led to some inequality between individuals which then led to envy, theft and violence. This was rapidly followed by the realisation that people needed to band together into village communities so that they could defend themselves from attack.

Whatever thoughts a reader may have about the spiritual and theological ideas given above, there can be no doubt about the scientific truth that our minds are better than we need and are therefore not the result of Darwinian Natural Selection. It is also self-evident that a physical process of Natural Selection could not have given people a soul. In the chapters which follow, there will be further exploration of these ideas, trying to keep to what is fair and reasonable both scientifically and theologically.

The writer hopes that you will read on, willing to be open to the ideas presented here and that you will come to your own conclusions in the light of what is written here.

Glossary

Abrahamic

This refers to Abraham, the founder of the Jewish religion, the first to worship One God.

The Abrahamic religions now include Judaism, Christianity and Islam.

Allele

An allele is one of a pair of genes that appear at a particular location on a particular chromosome and control the same characteristic.

Baryonic (matter)

A baryon is a type of composite subatomic particle belonging to the hadron family of particles. Baryonic matter refers to matter made of baryons. Strictly, this should only include protons, neutrons and all the objects composed of them, that is to say, atomic nuclei, but exclude things such as electrons and neutrinos which are leptons. In astronomy, the term baryonic matter is used loosely to mean all matter that consists of atomic nuclei and leptons.

Chromosome

A chromosome is a deoxyribonucleic acid molecule forming part of or all of the genetic material of an organism together with some supporting proteins.

Chandrasekhar limit

This is the maximum mass of a stable white dwarf star. It is now accepted to be 1.4 times the mass of the sun. Any white dwarf with less than this mass will remain a white dwarf but those with a larger mass will end as supernovae.

DNA RNA messenger RNA

DNA stands for deoxyribonucleic acid. This is a self-replicating nucleic acid molecule which is the main material of chromosomes and the carrier of genetic information.

RNA stands for ribonucleic acid. This is a nucleic acid which acts as a messenger carrying instructions from DNA for controlling the synthesis of proteins. (In some viruses, RNA carries the genetic code instead of DNA.)

Messenger RNA is the form of RNA in which genetic information, transcribed from DNA as a sequence of bases, is transferred to a ribosome.

Enlightenment

The Age of Enlightenment was an intellectual and philosophical movement in Western history and culture that is usually dated from 1715 to 1789 (or longer).

It followed the Renaissance and was concerned mainly with science, mathematics and technology.

Epistemology

The theory of knowledge, especially with regard to its methods, validity and scope, and the distinction between justified belief and opinion.

EvoDevo

This stands for evolutionary developmental biology. It is concerned with the comparative development of embryos of different species mediated by switching genes on and off.

Gene

A gene is a DNA sequence located on a chromosome. It mediates the transmission of information about one or more traits from one generation to the next.

Genome

The complete set of genes or genetic material present in a cell or organism.

Genotype

An organism's genotype is its full hereditary information.

Hadron

A subatomic composite particle composed of two quarks held together by the strong force.

Hermeneutics

The branch of knowledge that deals with interpretation, especially of the Bible or literary texts.

Isotropic

Having the same dimension when measured in different directions.

Lepton

Leptons are elementary particles: that is they appear not to be made up of smaller units of matter. They can either carry one unit of electric charge or be neutral.

Meiosis

Meiosis is a form of cell division that results in four daughter cells, each with half the number of chromosomes of the parent cell nucleus. It occurs during the formation of gametes. A diploid cell produces four haploid cells.

Mitochondria

Mitochondria are intra-cellular organelles which act rather like a digestive system for the cell, by taking in nutrient molecules, breaking them down and creating energy rich products. This process is called cellular respiration. They are present in the egg but not in sperm, so are transmitted only through the female line.

Mitosis

Mitosis is a form of cell division that results in two daughter cells each having the same number and kind of chromosomes as the parent nucleus. This is the cell division of normal tissue growth. A diploid cell produces two more diploid cells.

Monotheistic

Monotheistic means belief in One God. This is in distinction to belief in many Gods, which is called Pantheism; a Pantheon of Gods as in the ancient Greek and Roman cultures.

Muhammad PBUH

Muhammad was the founder of the Islamic religion. There are now many different ways of spelling his name, including Mahomet and Mohammed. He is known as the last of the five great Universal prophets (Abraham, Noah, Moses, Jesus and Muhammad PBUH).

The letters PBUH stand for "Peace be upon him" and are traditionally added to his name. He was born about 570 and died June 8th 632 (Christian era)

Ontology

The branch of metaphysics dealing with the nature of being. At its simplest, it is the study of existence. Ontology precedes epistemology: something has to exist before you can know about it.

Periodic table

The periodic table of the elements arranges all the known chemical elements in a table in an informative way. It was first started by Dimitri Mendeleev, a Russian chemist, when many elements were unknown, and has been fully developed later. It lists the elements in increasing order of atomic number.

Phenotype

Phenotype is an organism's observed properties including morphology, function, behaviour and development.

Prion

Prions are miss-folded proteins. They are able to transmit their miss-folded shape into normal examples of the same protein.

Pulsar

A pulsar is a rapidly rotating neutron star that emits regular pulses of radio waves.

Quasar

A quasar is a very massive and extremely remote celestial object that emits exceptionally large amounts of energy. It looks like a star when viewed with a telescope. It is thought that quasars contain massive black holes.

Quinarian system

This was a system of classifying animals according to a series of circles based on the number five. It was promoted by William Sharp Macleay and obtained some support in the first half of the nineteenth century but quickly fell into disrepute.

Renaissance

The Renaissance was a period of revival of European art and literature following earlier classical models, extending from the 14th to the 16th centuries.

It led to the Age of Enlightenment.

Ribosome

A ribosome is a complex cellular mechanism within all cells. It carries out protein synthesis by linking amino acids together in an order specified by the codons of messenger RNA.

Singularity

A gravitational singularity is a location in space-time where the gravitational field of a celestial body is predicted to become infinite by general relativity in a way that does not depend on the coordinate system.

Transcription

In biology this refers to the process of copying the information in a strand of DNA into a new molecule of messenger RNA. Reverse transcription is the opposite.

Teleological

Explanation of phenomena in terms of the purpose they serve rather than the cause by which they arose.

In theology, it relates to the doctrine of design and purpose in the material world.

Telomere

A telomere is a compound structure at the end of a chromosome which protects the end of the chromosome and prevents chromosomes from sticking together. This protects genetic information during cell division because a short piece of DNA is lost every time the DNA is replicated. Chromosomes get shorter each time a cell divides and eventually they get too short to function properly. This leads to cells ageing. The telomeres are an ageing clock in each cell.

Part One

1. Science and Theology

Definitions

In this chapter, we will think about science and theology and religion: what do we mean by these words and how do these concepts affect our lives. Theology is defined in the Oxford English Dictionary as "The study of the nature of God and religious belief." It is defined perhaps rather more helpfully in Wikipedia as "Systematic and rational study of concepts of deity and of the nature of religious truths." Religion is defined in the OED as "Recognition on the part of man of some higher unseen power as having control of his destiny, and as being entitled to obedience, reverence and worship; the general mental and moral attitude resulting from this belief: with reference to its effect upon the individual or the community: personal or general acceptance of this feeling as a standard of spiritual and practical life." Many other definitions have been proposed by scholars, depending on how inclusive or exclusive they thought that religion should be. For most people, religion means some form of belief in God, and the traditions, practices and moral rules that go with it. Unfortunately the word religion has some negative associations with some people nowadays, such as the idea that it is used to control and manipulate people, or to give too much wealth and power to certain people and may be used to promote sexual inequality. At times, it is associated with extreme violence and cruelty. There are justifiable criticisms that can be made about the way some religious people behave, but this does not support any criticism of God. It is the people who are doing the wrong, not God. In this book, the word "religion" is simply used to indicate belief in God, not tied to any particular faith or denomination. So where the word religion is used here, think also of the word theology. Do not start to think about the conflicts between religions and the dreadful things that religious people sometimes do. Those are completely separate issues. The issue here is belief in God. Do you believe in God? People who do not believe in God necessarily say that theology is the study of what people have imagined about God, but to a believer in God it is important that theology is about the real nature of God, not about what people think about God. Belief in God comes from a person's interaction with God and their ideas about the nature of God come from that. This is a very personal knowledge, which for the Abrahamic religions is built around the words that can be read in the Bible and Qur'an.

The OED defines science firstly as "A branch of study which is concerned either with a connected body of demonstrated truths or with observed facts systematically classified and more or less collegiated by being brought under general laws and which include trustworthy methods for the discovery of new truth within its own domain." It goes on to offer a second definition, which it says is now the dominant sense in ordinary use. "Often treated as synonymous with 'Natural and Physical Science', and thus restricted to those branches of study that relate to the phenomena of the material universe and their laws, sometimes with the implied exclusion of pure mathematics." For most people science is the study, description and investigation of the material world, and that is the meaning used in this book.

Conflict between science and religion

It is unfortunate that there seems to be a lot of controversy and conflict about the relationship between religion and science, now sometimes even referred to as "the war between science and religion". It has been like this for several centuries, starting with antagonism towards science by the Church, when science was first developing, but now being waged by atheists against religion. But this should not be necessary and is based on misconceptions about what religion and science really are. These conflicts do not seem to trouble Islam and Judaism, or other world religions as much as they do Christianity. It seems that the Christian church is now particularly exposed to attacks from those who think that science can in some way disprove God. Perhaps this is partly because Christianity demands belief in some miraculous events, which cannot of course be explained by science. There is also much more active teaching of science in many of the Christian countries than elsewhere in the world. This conflict has led to the publication of a lot of ideas and even to the development of some groups and institutions and a Chair at the University of Oxford devoted to "Religion and Science".

Religion is really the application of theological ideas to practical living, as seen by various groups of people and interpreted and manifested by them in a wide spread of practices, depending on their theological beliefs. The supposed conflict should therefore be referred to not as science and religion, but as science and theology.

The working disciplines of science and theology are completely separate. It is important that they are not muddled up. But it must be stressed that this does not mean that science is in some way in competition with God. That would be absolutely the wrong idea. God has no competitor. God encompasses all science. God made everything, including all the laws of science which control the way in which the physical world functions. Of course a religious person lives in the physical world, with a physical body, and acknowledges the physical world created by God, and that this physical world can, to an increasing extent, be understood by the use of scientific inquiry. But religion and theology do not seek to analyse the physical world in the way that science does, and they have no tools for doing so. They are concerned with God, the soul and the spiritual world.

Albert Einstein is said to have once remarked that science without religion is blind, but religion without science is lame. At first sight, this might seem to be a reasonable, even helpful view, as one might expect from Einstein: each can inform us, but they cannot constrain each other. But in fact religion has no effect on science, because the methodology of religion is completely distinct from that of science. It is only that religious ideas (or lack of them) may affect the *people* who work in science and therefore may affect their attitudes to their work. In the same way, science can have no effect on religion, because the methods of science cannot impinge upon the world of the spirit. Science has no way of detecting or interacting with the world of the spirit. The two disciplines are completely separate, using totally different methods. Science is constantly seeking new information; seeking change in our knowledge of how things work. Theology does not seek new knowledge or change, although it may consider the meaning of new interpretations of existing texts.

Separation of science from theology

Science depends on observation, measurement and calculation. Theology uses none of those things. Theology depends on revelation, interpretation and faith. These are not used in science. Therefore there can be no conflict between the findings of these two disciplines because there is no common methodology: just as there cannot be a conflict, for example, between music and painting.

To elaborate on that idea, it is not a perfect analogy but it goes some way to illustrate the point. When someone hears a violin playing, it is vibration of the air affecting their ear drums that causes the brain to produce the imagining of a musical sound. This is a very fleeting moment as the music progresses, it has no permanence. When looking at an oil painting, the eye reacts to the varying wavelengths of light reflected from the painted surface, which is a solid and long-lasting structure, which can hold the attention for some seconds or even minutes. So there are important differences between the two disciplines of music and painting, and the effects they have on the listener or observer. If someone thought that the violinist had played a note wrongly, it would be meaningless for them to say that they should have made it a darker green. Or if someone thought the colour green used by an artist was not right for that oak tree leaf, it would be without meaning if they said that it should have been painted a semitone higher. In the same way, it is not possible to use scientific procedures to comment on religion, or *vice versa*. The only correct way to discuss theology is by using theological arguments, not scientific ones. Regrettably, well known atheist polemicists try to use scientific data to argue against the existence of God when they should be using theological arguments, but they seldom do so.

The only points of contact between science and theology are those which are concerned with the philosophical ideas and principles which underlie and support science and theology, as developed by Torrance and later by McGrath. Here there are some useful comparisons that can be made, as will be discussed more fully later, but at the practical, working level, there is no connection between science and theology.

Stephen Jay Gould, the highly regarded Harvard palaeontologist, described what he called the non-overlapping magisteria of science and religion. By magisterium, he meant an area of competency or field of authority. He said that science deals with the "empirical realm" but religion deals with "questions of ultimate meaning". He wrote very convincingly and correctly about this. Sadly he died of cancer in 2002 at the age of 60, so he was unable to continue supporting this view. He was right to point out the lack of overlap. But it is not only that, but the fact that their working methodologies are entirely different and that theological propositions cannot be tested. That is widely accepted but not everybody agrees, for example Professor Alistair McGrath, Master of Wycliffe Hall, Oxford, the very distinguished philosopher and theologian, has preferred the term "partially overlapping magisteria", because of some underlying philosophical considerations, which are discussed below.

Critical Realism

There are now many philosophers who are interested in Critical Realism. Roy Bhaskar (1944–2014) is credited with starting this movement although the term was in use for some time before him, starting with a group of American philosophers around 1920. He developed statements concerning the philosophy of science, and also a special philosophy of human science, which modified the former due to the special nature of human society. These two strands have been combined, by others, to form the subject of "critical realism" as it is now known. This has been developed widely in many areas of thought, especially in the social sciences.

The theologian Andrew Wright published a book in 2013 called *Christianity and Critical Realism* (1) in which he gave great insight into Critical Realism. He supports the concept that theological propositions should be subject to rigorous appraisal, in a way similar to scientific propositions. He wrote "If critical realism is correct in suggesting that we make sense of the world by developing explanatory models that we are justified in embracing until such time as they are trumped by more powerful and comprehensive models, then any evaluation of the Christian retroductive explanation of the ultimate order-of-things must necessarily be cognisant of its ontological substance and epistemic ground. This being the case, any informed debate needs to engage with Christian ontology and epistemology with the same intellectual rigour and thoroughness granted any other field of intellectual endeavour." He emphasises the truth of the proposition that ontology has priority over epistemology, writing "Since the Enlightenment, Western philosophy has tended to misconstrue the relationship between ontology and epistemology. Modernity tends to restrict reality to our knowledge of reality, founded on either idealised concepts or empirical sense data: we know an object because we have a clear and distinct idea of it, or because we can experience it directly through our five senses. Nothing can be deemed 'real' unless it conforms to one or other of these two criteria. Post-modernity, as the flip-side of this modernist coin, tends to deny that our language and sense experiences possess any substantial epistemic purchase on ontological reality: in its soft form it affirms a thoroughgoing scepticism about the possibility of knowledge of external reality, while in its hard form it asserts a systematic anti-realism that denies the existence of any reality beyond the language employed by individuals' sceptical and fractured consciousnesses. Both positions seek to fulfil the Cartesian-driven quest for epistemic closure, which holds that knowledge of reality is absolutely certain (modernity) or absolutely uncertain (post-modernity)."

Andrew Wright wrote further "In highlighting the limitations of modern idealism and empiricism and of post-modern pragmatism and anti-realism, Bhaskar sought to provide the natural and human sciences with a sound theoretical and practical basis, and thereby enhance the project of human flourishing and liberation." He went on to write that Critical Realism "Seeks to map a path beyond the extremes of modern certainty and post-modern scepticism via a triumvirate of core philosophical principles: ontological realism, epistemic relativism and judgemental rationality. Ontological realism asserts that reality exists for the most part independently of human perception. Epistemic relativism asserts that our knowledge of reality is limited and contingent, and judgemental rationality asserts that it is nevertheless possible to judge between conflicting truth claims while recognising that all such judgements necessarily remain open to further adjudication."

"…According to ontological realism, objects exist and events occur in reality whether we are aware of them or not. A primary condition for human knowledge is the ontologically grounded distinction between the intransitive realm of real objects and events and the transitive realm of our contingent knowledge of them. If our (epistemic) knowledge of dinosaurs is accurate, then dinosaurs must have existed (ontologically) prior to our establishing knowledge of them. To deny this is to slip into the epistemic fallacy of reducing reality to our knowledge of reality. It is certainly true that we construct accounts of dinosaurs, but palpably untrue that in doing so we construct dinosaurs themselves. Epistemic relativism asserts the priority of ontology over epistemology: reality precedes knowledge of reality, so that we cannot know something unless there is first something to know. The affirmation of epistemic relativism acknowledges the limits of our knowledge, but does not deny either the actuality of genuine knowledge or the possibility of establishing better knowledge in the future. Judgemental rationality asserts that accounts of reality are not all of equal value: it is possible to judge some to be more truthful than others. There are no secure foundations on which to construct knowledge, and no protected procedures with which to adjudicate between conflicting truth claims. The empiricist appeal to verifiable sense data, the idealist appeal to logical coherence, and the romantic appeal to intuitive sensibility—together with its close relation the post-modern appeal to personal preferences and desires—have all been found wanting."

A special branch of critical realism is Theological Critical Realism. A leading figure in this was Michael Polanyi (1891–1976), a scientist who turned his attention to theology. His ideas were enlarged upon by the theologian T F Torrance (1913–2007) who has had a strong influence on contemporary Christian theology. In the United States Bernard Lonergan (1904–1984), the Jesuit theologian, has been very influential in developing critical realism. He made the practical observation that critical realists "must be attentive, intelligent, reasonable and responsible" in the way they work. Other important names in theological critical realism are Ian Barbour (1923–2013), Arthur Peacocke (1924–2006) and John Polkinghorne (1930–2021). They seek to show that there are similarities between the language of science and Christian theology, which they think should enable a dialogue to take place between the two. Alister McGrath has written much on this subject, agreeing with this view.

These writers take a deeply philosophical view of both science and theology. It is of course true that both disciplines share the goal of understanding the nature of the reality of the physical and spiritual worlds respectively, and both need an intellectual approach that is efficient and unbiased. But it seems to me that the similarities largely stop at that point. The nature of the object studied determines the methods used to study it. Science deals with the material (baryonic) world to the exclusion of the spiritual world. Theology deals only with the spiritual world, although recognising the existence of a material world. Because of this, the methodologies of the two disciplines are completely separate and distinct. But the most important difference is that science uses tests, which theology cannot do. If someone makes a scientific proposition, it will be tested by experiment and observation followed by mathematical calculation to see if it gives the expected results and accurate predictions. That cannot be done with a theological proposition because in the absence of measurable quantities mathematical calculations to test its accuracy cannot be done. This is why the paradigms of science are constantly changing as new knowledge makes it necessary to modify theories, but in theology there can be co-existence of conflicting paradigms because nobody has any hard data that could be used to prove with certainty (in the scientific sense) which ones are right or wrong. Therefore to attempt a comprehensive understanding of the totality of reality it is necessary to study both science and theology, concurrently but separately.

In the introduction to his book, Andrew Wright said that theological critical realism has paid little attention to Bhaskar's original ideas. He pointed out that it is necessary to try to understand the nature of the *whole* of reality, stating "The hermeneutical circle between parts and the whole requires that the interpreter makes sense of the parts of a text in the light of the text as a whole, and of the whole of the text in the light of its individual parts, in an ongoing interpretative dialectic. By extension, in seeking to make sense of reality the critical realist strives to understand the parts in terms of the whole, and the whole in terms of its constituent parts. This necessitates attempts to explain the ultimate nature of the *totality* of reality, regardless of whether the proffered explanations are religious/theological or secular/naturalistic. In acknowledging the intellectual imperative to attempt to make sense of the *totality* of experiences, objects/events and causal mechanisms, the spiritual turn in critical realism resonates strongly with the largely independent tradition of theological critical realism generated and nurtured by Christian theologians since the late 1950s."

However, in my view the need to study the totality of reality does nothing to bridge the gap between the disciplines of science and theology. Both are equally valid but distinct and separate ways of attempting to understand the nature of the material and spiritual worlds. For a believer in God, this totality of understanding has to be built up from separate scientific studies of the material world *and* theological studies of the spiritual world, placed side by side and viewed together to combine the findings of both into a non-conflicting scientific and theological world view. They must both be studied and they must both be seen as equally valid, equally prestigious and complementary to one another.

Critical realism is essentially nothing more than a guide to an efficient way of thinking. Andrew Wright wrote that it is really common sense. To repeat, as Bernard Lonergan stated, critical realists "must be attentive, intelligent, reasonable and responsible." That applies to any purposeful thinking about any subject. It may have been developed more in science than theology, because of the practical and experimental basis of science, but it is equally needed in business, commerce and all other intellectual activities. It does not imply similarity between science and theology just because both scientists and theologians should think efficiently.

Critical realism is not a good term to use but it has become entrenched in the literature. I think that a better term would be "Realistic Criticism". All theories, whether scientific or theological, should be subject to *realistic criticism*. All knowledge depends on contact between the knower and the object of enquiry. In the case of theology that can only be between an individual (one person) and God. In science, a group of people can share the observation of an event, such as an eclipse of the sun, or repeat experiments years later. In both cases, what is needed is rigorous analysis, not woolly thinking.

Theological Science

The Scottish Protestant theologian T. F. Torrance (1913–2007) wrote a book called *Theological Science.* (2) in 1969. He was not the first to use this term, which had been known for some decades previously. In the Preface, he quoted from his old teacher Professor A. E. Taylor. Torrance reported that in 1927 Taylor had "called for the locating of authority, [in theology] neither in individualism nor in some institutional seat, but in a reality that is wholly given and trans-subjective, and simply and absolutely authoritative through its givenness. If knowledge is to be more than personal opinion, Taylor argued, there must be control of our personal intellectual constructions by something which is not constructed but *received*. In our human knowledge of God, this is humbly to acknowledge that what is genuinely given has unquestionable right to control our thinking and acting, just because it is so utterly given to us and not made by us." This clarification of authority meant that it was possible to "entertain hope for the future of theology as a genuine, assured, and yet progressive science of God." That is absolutely correct, but the problem for each individual person and especially each theologian is to decide what is undoubtedly given and not something built up from within their own mind or the minds of others That, it seems to me, is the great difficulty which clearly separates theology from empirical science because of its lack of objective tests, even though there are now some new areas of scientific enquiry where objective tests cannot currently be made and perhaps may never be made.

Torrance continues (p.viii): "This is a book about the philosophy of the science of God…What is required of us here is not a Philosophy of Religion in which religion is substituted in the place of God, but a Philosophy of Theology in which we are directly engaged with knowledge of the Reality of God and not just with religious phenomenality. Whenever religion is substituted in the place of God, the fact that in religion we are concerned with the behaviour of *religious people,* sooner or later means the substitution of humanity in the place of religion." There is no substitute for the Philosophy of Theology "in which we are concerned with the meta-science of our direct cognitive relation with God." But it is not meta-science but meta-philosophy. Instead of talking about Theological science it might have been better to talk about Theological philosophy.

Torrance was absolutely correct that the discussion should not be between science and religion but between science and theology. He thought that one should look at the philosophical approaches that underpin both science and theology, the "philosophy of natural science" and the "philosophy of theological science". But therein lies the fallacy: to compare theology and the philosophy of theology with the philosophy of science, when the comparison should be between the practice of theology and the practice of science. The philosophy of science is not science. It is in considering the way in which a scientist or a theologian carries out their work that the clear differences emerge, overriding the undoubted underlying philosophical similarities which are of much lesser importance than the essential practical differences.

Torrance devotes the final chapter of his book to describing the similarities and differences between theology and science. He justifies the use of the term theological science by describing five key principles of thinking that can be applied to theology and science.

Similarities (edited and greatly abridged)

1. Theological science shares with the special sciences in being a *human inquiry.*
2. They both have respect for the *objectivity* of facts.
3. They both operate without any *preconceived* metaphysics.
4. They both recognise their *limitations*: that they come up against a line beyond which they cannot penetrate.
5. They both confront the difficulty of finding *language* that is capable of making clear the meaning of the new knowledge that is being found. Scientific thought reaches new concepts that cannot be expressed in any ordinary or natural language. Similar problems arise in theology, for example in the doctrine of Christ where there is an overlap of what is

accessible to historical determination and what is not determinable in some way.

These similarities are rather generalised principles that can be applied to many areas of constructive thought. A principle such as "objectivity" can be applied in most situations, and it is an important principle in the conduct of scientific enquiry, but objectivity itself is not science. Objectivity is useful in helping a scientist to do their work well.

Differences

Torrance wrote:

"There are differences between theological science and every other science due to the fact that theology has for its proper and primary object God Himself in his speaking and acting. All the other sciences deal with creaturely realities and only with aspects of being, whereas in theology we have to do also with the creative Source of all being.

"In all the other sciences, the human knower and the object known are both creaturely realities: they co-exist on the same creaturely plane and within the same framework of space and time. But can we presume upon an agreement of this kind between ourselves and that which infinitely transcends all creaturely reality even when we are brought to apprehend it?"

Torrance wrote much more on this theme but he did not emphasise the fact that theology lacks the observational evidence, experimentation and mathematics that are so important to the natural sciences. He would probably have said that those were in the realm of practical science, but that he was writing about the philosophy of science, not the way to carry out scientific work. He wrote a book of outstanding philosophical and theological power which has influenced many theologians.

I think that Torrance was strongly influenced by the development of quantum mechanics and string-theory that were under active discussion at the time when he was thinking about the content of his book. He refers to the Copenhagen Theory, which emanated from the Niels Bohr Institute in Copenhagen and was heavily committed to string-theory (see later in this chapter). It introduced new ideas and was at that time very controversial, for example the American theoretical physicist Richard P Feynman (1918–1988) who had made many valuable contributions, including the development of Perturbation Theory, wrote very critically about this, ridiculing the "believers" in the theory as though they were religious fanatics. In this, he did rather resonate with Torrance who thought that the developments in micro-physics meant that the subject was in some ways similar to theology in that it introduced the concept of the role of the observer as part of the enquiry into the order-of-things in a way that could affect the outcome.

Torrance wrote: "Thus it is apparent that theological and natural science share the same basic problem: how to refer our thoughts and statements genuinely beyond ourselves, how to reach knowledge of reality in which we do not intrude ourselves distortedly into the picture, and yet how to retain the full and integral place of the human subject in it all. When this is discerned, the dialogue between theology and science takes a different turn, for then they are seen to be allies in a common front where each faces the same insidious enemy, namely, man himself assuming the role of the Creator, acknowledging nothing except what he has made and declining to allow any of his constructions to be controlled by unconstructed reality beyond. Man and nature are here organically related and "God" is swallowed up between them."

Feynman was critical of the supporters of string-theory because he thought that they did not provide the mathematical basis that was required. He made the very profound observation that "The first principle [in physics] is that you must not fool yourself and you are the easiest person to fool." This really put so neatly what Torrance and other philosophers had been saying, but using many fewer words.

Later, Juan Maldacena in 1997 proposed an approach to understanding string theory and studying its properties by what is called the AdS/CFT correspondence. This supposed that there is correspondence between the anti-deSitter space and the Conformal Field Theory. This produces a theoretical result that implies that string theory is in some cases equivalent to a quantum field theory. It is said to provide insight into the mathematical structure of string theory and also provides insight into a number of aspects of quantum field theory in situations where traditional mathematical calculations are not effective. It represents a great advance in the understanding of string theory and quantum gravity by the specialists in this branch of physics. The AdS/CFT correspondence also (partially) resolves the so-called Black Hole Information Paradox, which had followed a publication by Stephen Hawking in 1975. It is also involved in studies of Quark-gluon plasma and quantum chromodynamics. At present, string theory does not have a mathematically rigorous formulation which would allow it to be defined precisely.

One of the obvious difficulties is that super-string theory supposes a Universe that has ten dimensions, and M-theory eleven dimensions, but we live in a world that evidently has only three spatial dimensions, plus time. In order to describe real physical phenomena using string theory, one must therefore imagine scenarios in which these extra dimensions would not be observed in experiments. One way to do this is called Compactification, in which some of the extra dimensions are assumed to "close up" on themselves to form circles. This can be used to construct models in which space-time is effectively four-dimensional. But not all the ways of compactifying the extra dimensions result in a model with the right properties to describe nature. For a realistic model of particle physics, the compacted extra dimensions must be shaped like a Calabi-Yau manifold. This is a special space which is usually imagined to be six-dimensional in applications of string theory. These remarks give a brief insight into what is an immensely complex and evolving intellectual landscape. They are included here to counter the claim that science has got the answer to everything. Not so. We live in an age of uncertainty about the scientific nature of the physical world we live in. That need not be of concern. The important thing is for a believer to hold to their complete faith and trust in God.

It is evident that so far there is no wide based acceptance of the various varieties of string-theory and quantum mechanics. The proper way to view quantum mechanics and these other recent developments in theoretical physics is that we do not understand them yet and await further clarification before there can be any general acceptance of them. They may be replaced by other theories.

These subjects are all fascinating to read about but a generalist can only obtain the haziest idea about what they are. They are at the frontier of understanding and at the limit of observation or detection. What one can say about them is that they attempt to describe the physical world we live in; they are not concerned with theology. Philosophically they have similarities with theology but they have an overpowering difference:

Fundamental studies in physics are critically dependent on mathematics.

Theology makes no use of mathematics.

It is true that the philosophical *approaches* that underpin science and theology have principles in common, but the science *qua* science cannot be used in theology. In my view, when science reaches a point at which observations and measurements cannot any longer be used, in effect it ceases to be science as we understand the word because the methods of science can no longer be applied.

In science, it is essential to begin with an open and unbiased view and this must also be true of theology, but in theology it is much more difficult to separate oneself from the propositions that one supports because theological ideas impact so strongly on our most important feelings and innermost nature. Theoretical physicists are trying to understand the nature and structure of the physical world and how it works. This is completely different from theologians who are trying to know about the nature of God, who is not a material being, as Torrance taught us. In fact, I believe that theologians should not be trying to know details about the nature of God. We should only try to know about God in so far as it may help us to know how we should react and respond to God. The nature of God is not for us to know. What we do need to know is what we should do about God: how we should lead our lives so as to try to be in accord with the will of God.

Leaving to one side the deeply philosophical studies of science and theology, as discussed by Torrance, and later by McGrath, a failure to maintain an iron curtain between practical science and the practice of religion can lead to all sorts of misunderstandings, for example the difficulties over the theory of Intelligent Design (see below). It may be of value for theologians to debate the similarities in the philosophical background to science and theology, but at street level, where believers are likely to be confronted by atheists who claim that science disproves God, it is important not to let atheists persist in the misuse of science to support their views.

Natural theology

A precursor to the theory of intelligent design was the publication of an important book by William Paley (1743–1808) entitled *Natural Theology: or, Evidences of the Existence and Attributes of the Deity, Collected from the Appearances of Nature*. (3) Paley was an English churchman and philosopher who exerted a strong and long-lasting influence on contemporary thinking through his book *Principles of Moral and Political Philosophy*, and other works. He was also very active in support of the abolition of slavery (meaning the slavery of African people deported to North America, which was abolished by the British Navy under orders from the British Parliament) and he defended the right of the poor to steal, especially if they were in need of food. *Natural*

Theology was his last book, but he said it should be read first, so as to build a systematic understanding of his arguments.

Three types of theology are recognised by scholars. Revealed theology stems from people's religious experiences and from scripture. Transcendental theology is based upon *a priori* reasoning. Natural theology is based on the way in which the natural world gives insight into the nature of God and creation.

Paley argued that the general well-being and harmony that evidently exists in nature is evidence of God's design of the whole of creation. He famously used the example of a watch, to illustrate a complex mechanism that must have been made by design. Paley could not accept that an animal could have designed its own limb. His ideas were based on gross anatomy. Later, Charles Darwin's book *On Natural Selection* (4) was claimed to be able to explain the design of a limb, by its gradual development over a very long period of time, in a series of steps directed by the demands of the environment. But a designer would also have developed their design in a series of prototypes, tested under working conditions, so it would have looked the same. Neither Darwin nor Paley had knowledge of the biochemical pathways that maintain cell function at the molecular level: their observations were limited to the macroscopic. Paley's arguments can still be adapted and applied at the molecular level, using modern knowledge, and at sub-microscopic level they have yet to be comprehensively answered.

Natural Theology is of course ignored by those who do not believe in God, but believers should not have any reticence about glorifying the way in which the wonderful perfection of the world at large and our own bodies point to design and a designer. This is strongly supported by Islam. People are created for a purpose:

"Did you think that We had created you in play (without any purpose), and that you would not be brought back to Us?" *The Qur'an* Chapter 23, verse 115.

All the signs we see when observing the universe and our own bodies should lead us to be aware of the creative power of God:

"We will show them Our signs in the horizons and within themselves until it becomes clear to them that it is the truth." *The Qur'an* Chapter 41, verse 53.

The Qur'an also directs its readers to consider the way in which the universe was created:

"Or were they created from nothing? Or were they the creators (of themselves)? Or did they create the heavens and Earth?" *The Qur'an* Chapter 52, verse 35.

It is generally accepted that the universe could not be created out of nothing. Out of nothing, nothing comes. Could the universe have created itself? How could something create itself before it existed: that is not possible. Was the universe created by something that was itself created? If that had happened the question then moves back to what created the thing that created the universe? This would go back in an infinite regression of causes and is therefore untenable. This leaves the only alternative, that the universe was created by something uncreated. We know that God is uncreated. He has always been and always will be, with no beginning and no end. The rational conclusion is therefore that the universe was created by God who has always existed.

At the first instant of the creation, the four fundamental forces were all present, possibly combined into one force, but then separated. They have certain values relative to one another. The values of these fundamental forces are such that the universe can exist in its present form. If these values were even slightly different, the universe could not have formed in the way it has. For example:

Gravitational force. If lower, stars would not start thermonuclear fusion so would not shine. If higher, stars would burn too fast and burn out before life could develop.

Strong nuclear force. If it was weaker atoms with more than one proton would not form, so hydrogen would be the only element in the universe. If stronger, all elements lighter than iron would be rare so the elements on which life depend, carbon and oxygen, would not be available.

Electromagnetic coupling force. This is what attaches electrons to the nucleus of the atom. If it was weaker, electrons would not be held in orbit. If it was stronger, the planetary electrons would be so tightly bound to the nucleus that they would not form bonds with other atoms. Either of these would mean that molecules could not be formed so there would be no life.

Intelligent design

The Theory of Intelligent Design is based on the concept that there are "irreducibly complex" biochemical pathways in living cells. These only work when the whole cascade is in place, so they could not, by definition, have arisen by small steps directed by a process of Natural Selection because anything less than the whole cascade does not work and so therefore would confer no advantage. There are many such biochemical pathways, such as the Krebs Cycle and the biochemistry of the retina. At present, it is hard to explain how they came into existence. We await a detailed, credible description of how irreducibly complex molecular pathways occurred without design.

It is unfortunate that the concept of intelligent design has become politicised in the United States. It has been enthusiastically promoted by Christians there, and this has given the opportunity to have the theory classified as a religious concept and therefore banned from school teaching in the USA. This has had the regrettable effect of removing the concept from scientific debate. What scientists should say about intelligent design is that it must be studied at the molecular level. It is then a scientific concept that raises important questions about evolution. It deserves more scientific investigation. It deals with aspects of the physical world, not the world of the spirit, so it is not a theological proposition except in so far as the term "intelligent design" implies the presence of a designer. It points towards the presence of a designer but does not prove it. There are many scientific observations which at present are unexplained and could be thought to point towards the existence of God, but none should be used in that way because of the God of the gaps argument. Intelligent design is considered further in another chapter.

God of the gaps

Believers in God should not say that intelligent design proves the existence of God, for two reasons: firstly, nobody should try to prove the existence of God (see below) and secondly, because it runs into the "God of the gaps" difficulty.

The reasoning of the God of the gaps argument is this. If there is a natural event that cannot be explained by science, and it is therefore said that it must be due to God, this can lead to a situation where, as scientific knowledge increases there are fewer and fewer unexplainable scenarios, and therefore fewer and fewer places where God can be proved to act. This reasoning has been used against intelligent design.

The concept of intelligent design originated in response to the teleological arguments in the *Natural Theology* of Paley. It might be said, however, that it is unlikely that science will ever have a complete and satisfying answer to everything, but even if it did, this would not in any way disprove the existence of God. It would simply provide for two possibilities: either God or no God. It is also true that some of the "answers" that are available to us now are only understood by a small coterie of mathematicians, who can talk to each other but whose work nobody else understands, so that it has to be taken on trust by most people. At present it is unfinished work, controversial and largely unproven.

For example, the Standard Model of Particle Physics, which has been developed since the 1970s, is a set of theories about the electromagnetic, weak and strong nuclear interactions, which mediate the dynamics of the known sub-atomic particles. It is described mathematically by a "Lagrangian", the work of Joseph Louis Lagrange, who introduced a new approach to classical mechanics in 1788. A Lagrangian is a mathematical function which is concerned with motion and the difference between potential energy and kinetic energy. It is also used in quantum mechanics and String Theory. The Lagrangian associated with the theories of the Standard Model of Particle Physics looks like this.

$$\mathcal{L}_{SM} = -\tfrac{1}{2}\partial_\nu g^a_\mu \partial_\nu g^a_\mu - g_s f^{abc}\partial_\mu g^a_\nu g^b_\mu g^c_\nu - \tfrac{1}{4}g^2_s f^{abc}f^{ade}g^b_\mu g^c_\nu g^d_\mu g^e_\nu - \partial_\nu W^+_\mu \partial_\nu W^-_\mu -$$
$$M^2 W^+_\mu W^-_\mu - \tfrac{1}{2}\partial_\nu Z^0_\mu \partial_\nu Z^0_\mu - \tfrac{1}{2c^2_w}M^2 Z^0_\mu Z^0_\mu - \tfrac{1}{2}\partial_\mu A_\nu \partial_\mu A_\nu - igc_w(\partial_\nu Z^0_\mu(W^+_\mu W^-_\nu -$$
$$W^+_\nu W^-_\mu) - Z^0_\nu(W^+_\mu \partial_\nu W^-_\mu - W^-_\mu \partial_\nu W^+_\mu) + Z^0_\mu(W^+_\nu \partial_\nu W^-_\mu - W^-_\nu \partial_\nu W^+_\mu)) -$$
$$igs_w(\partial_\nu A_\mu(W^+_\mu W^-_\nu - W^+_\nu W^-_\mu) - A_\nu(W^+_\mu \partial_\nu W^-_\mu - W^-_\mu \partial_\nu W^+_\mu) + A_\mu(W^+_\nu \partial_\nu W^-_\mu -$$
$$W^-_\nu \partial_\nu W^+_\mu)) - \tfrac{1}{2}g^2 W^+_\mu W^-_\mu W^+_\nu W^-_\nu + \tfrac{1}{2}g^2 W^+_\mu W^-_\nu W^+_\mu W^-_\nu + g^2 c^2_w(Z^0_\mu W^+_\mu Z^0_\nu W^-_\nu -$$
$$Z^0_\mu Z^0_\mu W^+_\nu W^-_\nu) + g^2 s^2_w(A_\mu W^+_\mu A_\nu W^-_\nu - A_\mu A_\mu W^+_\nu W^-_\nu) + g^2 s_w c_w(A_\mu Z^0_\nu(W^+_\mu W^-_\nu -$$
$$W^+_\nu W^-_\mu) - 2A_\mu Z^0_\mu W^+_\nu W^-_\nu) - \tfrac{1}{2}\partial_\mu H \partial_\mu H - 2M^2 \alpha_h H^2 - \partial_\mu \phi^+ \partial_\mu \phi^- - \tfrac{1}{2}\partial_\mu \phi^0 \partial_\mu \phi^0 -$$
$$\beta_h\left(\frac{2M^2}{g^2} + \frac{2M}{g}H + \tfrac{1}{2}(H^2 + \phi^0 \phi^0 + 2\phi^+ \phi^-)\right) + \frac{2M^4}{g^2}\alpha_h -$$
$$g\alpha_h M(H^3 + H\phi^0 \phi^0 + 2H\phi^+ \phi^-) -$$
$$\tfrac{1}{8}g^2 \alpha_h(H^4 + (\phi^0)^4 + 4(\phi^+ \phi^-)^2 + 4(\phi^0)^2 \phi^+ \phi^- + 4H^2 \phi^+ \phi^- + 2(\phi^0)^2 H^2) -$$
$$gMW^+_\mu W^-_\mu H - \tfrac{1}{2}g\frac{M}{c^2_w}Z^0_\mu Z^0_\mu H -$$
$$\tfrac{1}{2}ig\left(W^+_\mu(\phi^0 \partial_\mu \phi^- - \phi^- \partial_\mu \phi^0) - W^-_\mu(\phi^0 \partial_\mu \phi^+ - \phi^+ \partial_\mu \phi^0)\right) +$$
$$\tfrac{1}{2}g\left(W^+_\mu(H\partial_\mu \phi^- - \phi^- \partial_\mu H) + W^-_\mu(H\partial_\mu \phi^+ - \phi^+ \partial_\mu H)\right) + \tfrac{1}{2}g\frac{1}{c_w}(Z^0_\mu(H\partial_\mu \phi^0 - \phi^0 \partial_\mu H) +$$
$$M\left(\tfrac{1}{c_w}Z^0_\mu \partial_\mu \phi^0 + W^+_\mu \partial_\mu \phi^- + W^-_\mu \partial_\mu \phi^+\right) - ig\frac{s^2_w}{c_w}MZ^0_\mu(W^+_\mu \phi^- - W^-_\mu \phi^+) + igs_w MA_\mu(W^+_\mu \phi^- -$$
$$W^-_\mu \phi^+) - ig\frac{1-2c^2_w}{2c_w}Z^0_\mu(\phi^+ \partial_\mu \phi^- - \phi^- \partial_\mu \phi^+) + igs_w A_\mu(\phi^+ \partial_\mu \phi^- - \phi^- \partial_\mu \phi^+) -$$
$$\tfrac{1}{4}g^2 W^+_\mu W^-_\mu(H^2 + (\phi^0)^2 + 2\phi^+ \phi^-) - \tfrac{1}{8}g^2 \frac{1}{c^2_w}Z^0_\mu Z^0_\mu(H^2 + (\phi^0)^2 + 2(2s^2_w - 1)^2 \phi^+ \phi^-) -$$
$$\tfrac{1}{2}g^2 \frac{s^2_w}{c_w}Z^0_\mu \phi^0(W^+_\mu \phi^- + W^-_\mu \phi^+) - \tfrac{1}{2}ig^2 \frac{s^2_w}{c_w}Z^0_\mu H(W^+_\mu \phi^- - W^-_\mu \phi^+) + \tfrac{1}{2}g^2 s_w A_\mu \phi^0(W^+_\mu \phi^- +$$
$$W^-_\mu \phi^+) + \tfrac{1}{2}ig^2 s_w A_\mu H(W^+_\mu \phi^- - W^-_\mu \phi^+) - g^2 \frac{s_w}{c_w}(2c^2_w - 1)Z^0_\mu A_\mu \phi^+ \phi^- -$$
$$g^2 s^2_w A_\mu A_\mu \phi^+ \phi^- + \tfrac{1}{2}ig_s \lambda^a_{ij}(\bar{q}^\sigma_i \gamma^\mu q^\sigma_j)g^a_\mu - \bar{e}^\lambda(\gamma \partial + m^\lambda_e)e^\lambda - \bar{\nu}^\lambda(\gamma \partial + m^\lambda_\nu)\nu^\lambda - \bar{u}^\lambda_j(\gamma \partial +$$
$$m^\lambda_u)u^\lambda_j - \bar{d}^\lambda_j(\gamma \partial + m^\lambda_d)d^\lambda_j + igs_w A_\mu\left(-(\bar{e}^\lambda \gamma^\mu e^\lambda) + \tfrac{2}{3}(\bar{u}^\lambda_j \gamma^\mu u^\lambda_j) - \tfrac{1}{3}(\bar{d}^\lambda_j \gamma^\mu d^\lambda_j)\right) +$$
$$\tfrac{ig}{4c_w}Z^0_\mu\{(\bar{\nu}^\lambda \gamma^\mu(1 + \gamma^5)\nu^\lambda) + (\bar{e}^\lambda \gamma^\mu(4s^2_w - 1 - \gamma^5)e^\lambda) + (\bar{d}^\lambda_j \gamma^\mu(\tfrac{4}{3}s^2_w - 1 - \gamma^5)d^\lambda_j) +$$
$$(\bar{u}^\lambda_j \gamma^\mu(1 - \tfrac{8}{3}s^2_w + \gamma^5)u^\lambda_j)\} + \tfrac{ig}{2\sqrt{2}}W^+_\mu\left((\bar{\nu}^\lambda \gamma^\mu(1 + \gamma^5)U^{lep}_{\lambda\kappa}e^\kappa) + (\bar{u}^\lambda_j \gamma^\mu(1 + \gamma^5)C_{\lambda\kappa}d^\kappa_j)\right) +$$
$$\tfrac{ig}{2\sqrt{2}}W^-_\mu\left((\bar{e}^\kappa U^{lep\dagger}_{\kappa\lambda}\gamma^\mu(1 + \gamma^5)\nu^\lambda) + (\bar{d}^\kappa_j C^\dagger_{\kappa\lambda}\gamma^\mu(1 + \gamma^5)u^\lambda_j)\right) +$$
$$\tfrac{ig}{2M\sqrt{2}}\phi^+\left(-m^\kappa_e(\bar{\nu}^\lambda U^{lep}_{\lambda\kappa}(1 - \gamma^5)e^\kappa) + m^\lambda_\nu(\bar{\nu}^\lambda U^{lep}_{\lambda\kappa}(1 + \gamma^5)e^\kappa) +$$
$$\tfrac{ig}{2M\sqrt{2}}\phi^-\left(m^\lambda_e(\bar{e}^\lambda U^{lep\dagger}_{\lambda\kappa}(1 + \gamma^5)\nu^\kappa) - m^\kappa_\nu(\bar{e}^\lambda U^{lep\dagger}_{\lambda\kappa}(1 - \gamma^5)\nu^\kappa) - \tfrac{g}{2}\frac{m^\lambda_\nu}{M}H(\bar{\nu}^\lambda \nu^\lambda) -$$
$$\tfrac{g}{2}\frac{m^\lambda_e}{M}H(\bar{e}^\lambda e^\lambda) + \tfrac{ig}{2}\frac{m^\lambda_\nu}{M}\phi^0(\bar{\nu}^\lambda \gamma^5 \nu^\lambda) - \tfrac{ig}{2}\frac{m^\lambda_e}{M}\phi^0(\bar{e}^\lambda \gamma^5 e^\lambda) - \tfrac{1}{4}\bar{\nu}_\lambda M^R_{\lambda\kappa}(1 - \gamma_5)\hat{\nu}_\kappa -$$
$$\tfrac{1}{4}\bar{\nu}_\lambda M^R_{\lambda\kappa}(1 - \gamma_5)\hat{\nu}_\kappa + \tfrac{ig}{2M\sqrt{2}}\phi^+\left(-m^\kappa_d(\bar{u}^\lambda_j C_{\lambda\kappa}(1 - \gamma^5)d^\kappa_j) + m^\lambda_u(\bar{u}^\lambda_j C_{\lambda\kappa}(1 + \gamma^5)d^\kappa_j) +$$
$$\tfrac{ig}{2M\sqrt{2}}\phi^-\left(m^\lambda_d(\bar{d}^\lambda_j C^\dagger_{\lambda\kappa}(1 + \gamma^5)u^\kappa_j) - m^\kappa_u(\bar{d}^\lambda_j C^\dagger_{\lambda\kappa}(1 - \gamma^5)u^\kappa_j) - \tfrac{g}{2}\frac{m^\lambda_u}{M}H(\bar{u}^\lambda_j u^\lambda_j) -$$
$$\tfrac{g}{2}\frac{m^\lambda_d}{M}H(\bar{d}^\lambda_j d^\lambda_j) + \tfrac{ig}{2}\frac{m^\lambda_u}{M}\phi^0(\bar{u}^\lambda_j \gamma^5 u^\lambda_j) - \tfrac{ig}{2}\frac{m^\lambda_d}{M}\phi^0(\bar{d}^\lambda_j \gamma^5 d^\lambda_j) + \bar{G}^a \partial^2 G^a + g_s f^{abc}\partial_\mu \bar{G}^a G^b_\mu g^c_\mu +$$
$$\bar{X}^+(\partial^2 - M^2)X^+ + \bar{X}^-(\partial^2 - M^2)X^- + \bar{X}^0(\partial^2 - \tfrac{M^2}{c^2_w})X^0 + \bar{Y}\partial^2 Y + igc_w W^+_\mu(\partial_\mu \bar{X}^0 X^- -$$
$$\partial_\mu \bar{X}^+ X^0) + igs_w W^+_\mu(\partial_\mu \bar{Y}X^- - \partial_\mu \bar{X}^+ Y) + igc_w W^-_\mu(\partial_\mu \bar{X}^- X^0 -$$
$$\partial_\mu \bar{X}^0 X^+) + igs_w W^-_\mu(\partial_\mu \bar{X}^- Y - \partial_\mu \bar{Y}X^+) + igc_w Z^0_\mu(\partial_\mu \bar{X}^+ X^+ -$$
$$\partial_\mu \bar{X}^- X^-) + igs_w A_\mu(\partial_\mu \bar{X}^+ X^+ -$$
$$\partial_\mu \bar{X}^- X^-) - \tfrac{1}{2}gM\left(\bar{X}^+ X^+ H + \bar{X}^- X^- H + \tfrac{1}{c^2_w}\bar{X}^0 X^0 H\right) + \tfrac{1-2c^2_w}{2c_w}igM\left(\bar{X}^+ X^0 \phi^+ - \bar{X}^- X^0 \phi^-\right) +$$
$$\tfrac{1}{2c_w}igM\left(\bar{X}^0 X^- \phi^+ - \bar{X}^0 X^+ \phi^-\right) + igMs_w\left(\bar{X}^0 X^- \phi^+ - \bar{X}^0 X^+ \phi^-\right) +$$
$$\tfrac{1}{2}igM\left(\bar{X}^+ X^+ \phi^0 - \bar{X}^- X^- \phi^0\right).$$

It requires a deep knowledge of mathematics to understand this and the meaning of it must be clear to very few people. Meanwhile the Standard Model of Particle Physics does not account for everything and work continues, to try to make it of universal application.

Physicists would like to have a Standard Theory of Everything!

Newton's theory of gravity gave accurate predictions and was accepted for several hundred years, until Einstein published his Special Theory of Relativity and General Theory of Relativity in 1905 and 1916. Newton's theory supposed a force of attraction associated with a massive body. It is now thought that the gravitational effect is produced by the effect that the body has on the space which surrounds it, as described in Einstein's theories. Work on the structure of the atom led to the elucidation of Quantum Mechanics which describe the motion of sub-atomic particles. It was then seen that the laws that govern matter on a very large scale were not compatible with the laws that govern matter on a very small scale: gravity and quantum mechanics. Theoretical physicists wished to find a way to resolve this, and towards the end of the last century a new theory was proposed called String Theory. This supposes that a fundamental particle is not a "point" but a "string". It has length and it vibrates in two dimensions. The wave form of the string determines the nature of the particle. This was regarded as a great advance at the time, but still did not solve the difficulty with gravity. It was followed by the so-called Super-string Theory, which does embrace gravity. There are now several string theories and a combined theory called M-theory. At the time of writing, the whole subject is still very controversial and is under intense scrutiny. When working with very small particles at sub-atomic level it is not always possible to make observations or measurements. There are experiments that physicists would like to do that would require much higher energies than available today, even with the Large Hadron Collider. Where theories are being proposed in a situation where observations and measurements cannot always be made, the scientist is to some extent in a similar situation to the theologian. However, this does not in any way blur the clear distinction between science and theology because the theoretical physicist is trying to understand the Physical World whereas the theologian is trying to understand God and the Spiritual World. Most people have to take all this on trust and it is surprising that they do so, except that it does not matter to their everyday lives whether the mathematicians have got it right or not.

Returning to the "God of the gaps", this concept is in itself faulty. It requires only a few seconds' thought to realise that God is not limited in his actions to things which we do not understand. God is active in everything that he wants to be active in. Where we have some understanding of a process that is simply an insight into the way in which God deals with that process. Understanding the process does not exclude God. The mistake is in trying to use science to prove the existence of God which is just as wrong as trying to use science to disprove the existence of God.

The late Stephen Hawking, the celebrated Cambridge mathematician, said in 2010 that he was close to being able to show how the universe began without the *need* for God. "No need to have someone light the blue touch paper" he said. (And "Who made the firework?" one might ask.) But he ignored some basic logic: just because something *could* be done without God does not mean that it *was* done without God. If there was a situation where, beyond any doubt, there was no scientific explanation, and never would be any scientific explanation, then it might be reasonable to conclude that it *must* be due to God. (This was the situation people were in before there was any science). In the absence now of any such scenario, the conclusion must be that any event could be either due to God or not due to God. It presents two possibilities, where previously (before the advance of science) there was only the one. But there remain the two possibilities, and it is intellectually false to pretend, as some atheists do, that there is only one: that because science can explain something, there is no God. But equally it is wrong for believers in God to say that because there is currently no scientific explanation for something, it proves the existence of God. That is the wrong approach and leads to the God of the gaps difficulty.

An individual person's choice between these two: God or no God, depends on knowledge of God or no knowledge of God. It is a choice based on a person's whole experience of life, including the influence of their parents, school and peers. Above all it is a personal response to God, either turning to God or turning away from God.

The choice between God and no God is very stark:

WITH GOD: Living a life knowing God and being in constant communication with God, being guided through life's choices by God and having eternal life in the warmth of God's love.

OR

WITHOUT GOD: Living a life in an unfeeling and hostile world without values or purpose, directed only by the result of chemical interactions, alone, vulnerable and time limited to the seconds of conscious physical existence.

With some people it may be not so much a choice about God as a refusal to believe in a non-material world. If someone believes that nothing exists except that which can be detected by physical methods, then belief in God is automatically ruled out, because God is everlasting so therefore is not a physical being. God is not a physical being therefore God cannot be detected by science and no one should expect God to be detected by science. That is why science is not relevant to this question.

An analogy of the way in which "science" *cannot* detect something which *does* exist can be illustrated like this. If a piece of cardboard is placed over a magnet, and iron filings are sprinkled over the card, when the card is tapped the iron filings will line up along the lines of magnetic force made by the magnet. If the card is replaced with a clean one, and the procedure repeated using filings of gold, when the card is tapped the gold filings will not move. They are undetected by the magnet which does not have the ability to interact with gold. If one imagines the magnet being able to talk, it might say "I believe in iron, I can detect it and move it around, but I do not believe in gold because I cannot find any evidence for its existence." This is analogous to the way in which atheists use science. Atheists say that because science cannot detect the world of the spirit, it does not exist. They ignore the simple fact that science can only detect baryonic matter, it does not have the tools to detect the world of the spirit, but that does not mean that the spiritual world does not exist. People can detect spirituality and be aware of it at certain times.

As recently as the middle of the nineteenth century it was thought that atoms could not be split into smaller subunits. Later it was discovered that atoms were quite complex structures, especially the atoms higher in the Periodic Table. An atom consists of a nucleus which is made up of protons and neutrons. There are electrons which circle round the nucleus like planets round the sun. The number of protons in the nucleus and corresponding number of electrons determines the nature of the matter that the atom makes: for example Oxygen has an atomic number of 8 and Nitrogen 14. It was first thought that the structure of the atom could not be broken down any further but now it is known that protons are made from what are called quarks. Electrons are what are called leptons. These are thought to be fundamental particles which cannot be broken down into anything smaller. Elements can exist as different isotopes of the same atom, depending on the number of electrons.

The Standard Model of Particle Physics describes the fundamental particles which are thought to explain all matter in the universe. There are two groups of particles in the Standard Model. These are fermions and bosons. Matter is made from fermions. Bosons carry the electromagnetic force and the strong and weak nuclear forces between fermions. Fermions are divided into two classes called quarks and leptons. These particles exist in what are called "generations". There are three generations of quarks and leptons.

The quarks have been given rather fanciful names which might be thought rather disrespectful to entities of such fundamental importance. The first-generation quarks are called "Up quarks" and "Down quarks". The second-generation quarks are called "Charm" and "Strange" and the third-generation quarks are called "Top" and "Bottom". The quarks make up the protons and neutrons in the atomic nucleus.

The fermions that are called leptons also have two forms in each generation. First generation leptons are electrons and electron neutrinos. In the second generation, there are the muon and muon neutrino. In the third generation, there are the tau and tau neutrino. Quarks interact with the strong nuclear force but leptons do not.

Bosons are presently put into five categories: Gluon, Photon, W boson, Z boson and the Higgs boson. The photon carries the electromagnetic force which is responsible for the electromagnetic radiation, electric fields and magnetic fields. The gluon carries the strong nuclear force. This is what joins quarks together to make larger composite particles. The W and Z bosons carry the weak nuclear force. The Higgs boson is thought to confer mass on other particles.

The three generations of fermions differ in mass. The first-generation fermions have less mass than the second, which has less mass than the third. The first generation: the electrons, up and down quarks and neutrinos form the matter that we are made of. Each fundamental particle has its corresponding anti-particle. These have the same mass as the particle but opposite charge.

The fundamental particles are subject to the Pauli Exclusion Principle proposed by the Austrian physicist Wolfgang Pauli in 1925. This means that two fermions cannot occupy the same quantum state as each other. If two fermions were close together, they would have to have different velocities and move away from each other. Because of the Pauli Exclusion Principle electrons have to orbit the nucleus of the atom in distinct paths, known as "electron shells" so that they are in a different quantum state to the others. The Pauli Exclusion Principle also ensures that matter does not collapse in on itself even though the attractive forces between particles are greater than the repulsive forces.

Quantum theory

Quantum theory is concerned with the physics of the very small: the behaviour of atoms and their sub-units. Classical physics deals with the behaviour of matter and energy on the large scale, the kind of quantities we use in every-day life when we buy a sack of potatoes. But the principles of classical physics do not work when applied to the very small. Quantum theory (also called Quantum mechanics, although that is really the mathematical aspects of the subject) is one of the most successful theories in science. Despite that, it is not fully understood or agreed by leading contemporary physicists. There are four principles that are the essentials of quantum theory. These are: (1) Energy comes in small discrete units called photons. (2) Elementary particles behave both like particles and like waves. (3) Particle motion is random. (4) Particle position and momentum cannot be known at the same time.

The idea that light was emitted as discrete packets of energy was first proposed in 1900 by Max Planck in a lecture to the German Physics Society. He called these packets of energy "quanta" (derived from the word quantity). Later, Einstein described these quanta as streams of particles which he called "photons", and this is the name used now.

Elementary particles may exist as particles or waves and it is not possible to know which they are until the moment when they are observed. Only then can one know which they are, at that moment. Before measurement, all that can be said is that there is a certain probability that the object is in state A or B. It is only at the moment when the measurement is made that a choice is made about which of these possible states the object will possess. Einstein was not willing to accept that the world could be so uncertain. He is reported to have said "God does not play dice," to which Niels Bohr is said to have replied "Einstein, don't tell God what to do." The German physicist Werner Heisenberg proposed in 1927 what is called the Uncertainty Principle. The momentum and position of an object are limited. When we measure a quantum position, its momentum is uncertain. The more accurately the position is known the less precise will be the measurement of momentum.

Einstein's contemporaries Niels Bohr, Werner Heisenberg and Erwin Schrodinger developed a mathematical description of the quantum world in the 1920s in which certainties were replaced by probabilities. They argued that all we can know about a quantum system is what we can measure. This is generally accepted now. It is not necessary to understand quantum theory completely before using it in practical applications. These include the development of touch-screens for devices like computers and mobile telephones. It is expected to lead before long to the production of computers that are very much faster than at present.

The standard Model of Particle Physics is well established and apparently not too controversial, although there is something called the Weak Hierarchy problem which needs an explanation. The problem is a result of radiative corrections to the Higgs mass from hypothetical particles beyond the weak scale—whatever that means. The quantum theory is now well established but imperfectly understood. The next subject to consider is cosmology which is even more controversial, because it involves looking back in time for billions of years and trying to see and measure objects and events that are billions of light years away from us.

Cosmology

The Standard Model of Cosmology, that is the Lambda-CDM model, known informally as "The Big Bang", describes the origin of the universe. [Lambda is the Greek letter used to signify the Cosmological Constant. This arose from calculations in Einstein's General Theory of Relativity but he abandoned it in 1931 because Hubble had discovered the expanding universe. Despite that, it is used to express the energy density of space: vacuum energy. CDM stands for Cold Dark Energy.] This model replaces the Steady State theory that became untenable after the discovery of the cosmic microwave background around 1950. The Big Bang happened after the initial singularity, when there was a sudden expansion of space time, 13.7 billion years ago. The steps in this process are still speculative, especially in the first second. It will be some time before theoretical physics has developed enough to be more certain about them, but the following account, taken from several sources, represents a brief summary of what is currently thought to be conditionally correct by most physicists in 2020.

Planck Epoch

From zero to approximately 10^{-43} seconds. The four fundamental forces (Electromagnetic force, Strong nuclear force, Weak nuclear force and the force of gravity) were all present, possibly combined into one fundamental force, held together in perfect symmetry. At this time, the universe had a dimension of 10^{-35} metres and a temperature of 10^{32}°C.

Grand Unification Epoch

From 10^{-43} to 10^{-36} seconds. The force of gravity separates from the other fundamental forces, which remain unified. The earliest elementary particles and anti-particles begin to be made.

Inflationary Epoch

From 10^{-36} to 10^{-32} seconds. The strong nuclear force separates from the others, and this results in a very rapid expansion in the size of the universe, by a factor of 10^{26} or more, so that it increases in size to a diameter of 10 centimetres, about the size of a grapefruit. A quark-gluon plasma becomes thinly distributed throughout the universe. There is some support for an even greater inflation in size. At this time vacuum energy appeared, which caused gravity to become repulsive instead of attractive for about 10^{-32} seconds. This it is thought could have resulted in an amazing expansion by a factor of 10^{50}, which would have made the universe increase to a size of 18 billion light years. The inflationary epoch is especially controversial among cosmologists.

Electroweak Epoch

From 10^{-32} to 10^{-12} seconds. As the strong nuclear force separates from the other two, large numbers of exotic particles are produced, including W and Z bosons and Higgs bosons. Higgs bosons slow down particles which confers mass on them, enabling a universe that began as nothing but radiation to have mass.

Quark Epoch

From 10^{-12} to 10^{-6} seconds. The universe cools and the fundamental forces take on their present form. Quarks, electrons and neutrinos are formed in large numbers. Quarks and anti-quarks destroy each other when they collide, but some quarks are left over to combine together in what is called baryogenesis to form the basis of matter (hadrons).

Hadron Epoch

From 10^{-6} to one second. During this epoch the universe cools down to about a trillion degrees Celsius, which is cool enough for quarks to combine together to form hadrons, such as protons and neutrons. At the same time, electrons collide with protons to form neutrons, releasing mass-less neutrinos. These neutrinos travel freely through space, at near the speed of light, and are still observable today.

Lepton Epoch

From one second to three minutes. After most of the hadrons and anti-hadrons collide and destroy each other, leptons such as electrons and positrons make up most of the mass of the universe. Then electrons and positrons collide and annihilate each other, freeing energy in the form of photons. Colliding photons then create more electron-positron pairs.

Nucleosynthesis

From 3 minutes to 20 minutes. The universe cools further, down to about one billion degrees Celsius. At that temperature, protons and neutrons can combine through nuclear fusion to form the nuclei of atoms. The simplest elements are formed: hydrogen, helium and lithium. After about 20 minutes, the temperature and density of the universe has fallen to a point where nuclear fusion can no longer happen.

Photon Epoch

From 20 minutes to 240,000 years. This is a long period of continued cooling, during which the universe consists of plasma—a hot opaque soup of atomic nuclei and electrons. Photons form the main energy of the universe.

Recombination/Decoupling

From 240,000 years to 300,000 years. The temperature of the universe continues to fall, reaching about 3,000°C (similar to the surface of the sun) and its density also continues to fall. At this time ionised hydrogen and helium atoms capture electrons (recombination) thus neutralising their electric charge. Up to this time the universe has been opaque to light, but with electrons now bound to atoms, the universe becomes transparent to light. This is the earliest epoch observable today. The universe then contained about 75% hydrogen, 25% helium and a trace of lithium. It also released photons which had been interacting with electrons and protons—decoupling. These photons travel freely at near the speed of light and are seen now as the cosmic microwave background.

Dark Epoch

From 300,000 years to 150 million years. This is after the first atoms have formed but before there are any stars. There is nothing to produce light, so the universe is completely dark. There is only very diffuse matter remaining so activity is greatly reduced with low energy and slow changes. The universe is thought to have been mostly dark matter.

Reionisation

From 150 million years to one billion years. The first quasars form. (Quasars look like stars through a telescope. They are extremely remote from us and emit very powerful radiation. They are thought to contain enormous black holes.) The strong radiation they emit re-ionises the surrounding universe. It now consists of ionised plasma. Once stars form there will be light in the universe.

Star and galaxy formation began to occur after 300 to 500 million years. It is thought that there were small irregularities in the density of the primordial gas, and gravity acted on them to produce more and more dense objects, leading to the formation of stars when the cosmic gas collapsed under gravity to a point when it was hot enough to cause nuclear fusion reactions between hydrogen atoms. The first stars were very large and did not last long. They are known as Population III stars and were metal-free. They exploded as enormous supernovae. The debris from them was used again to form second generation stars (Population II), and then third generation stars (Population I). Gravitational attraction then drew the stars together into galaxies, and the galaxies into clusters of galaxies. Our Sun is a late generation star which has been formed out of debris from generations of earlier stars. It was formed, together with the solar system of planets around it, about 8.5 to 9 billion years after the Big Bang, that is, about 4.5 to 5.0 billion years ago. Today, 13.7 billion years after the Big Bang we still detect the cosmic microwave background radiation, there is continuous re-use of stellar materials as old stars decay and new stars are formed, and the universe continues to expand, at an ever-increasing rate. Present estimates are that there are at least one hundred billion galaxies in the observable universe. Some think that the figure is much higher. Our own galaxy contains about 200 billion stars. It has a diameter of about 100 light years. So far about 500 solar systems (with planets) have been found in our galaxy, but in total it is likely to contain as many as 100 billion planets.

Knowledge about cosmology is increasing all the time. One thing that has been puzzling cosmologists is that on theoretical grounds there is more normal matter in the universe than can be seen. Recently (2020) some observations have been reported which detect this diffuse matter. When radio waves travel through empty space, they all have the same speed, regardless of wavelength, but when traveling through matter the wavelength does affect the speed of travel. This effect has been used by astronomers in Western Australia, working with their own radio-telescope in collaboration with the Very Large Telescope in Chile. Fast Radio Bursts (FRBs) can be detected and the delay in the speed of some wavelengths can be measured. The position of the origin of the FRB can be seen with an optical telescope and its distance calculated. The distance multiplied by the delay in speed gives a figure for the density of the matter through which the radio waves have passed. In this way, it has been possible to detect diffuse "missing matter" in many directions from Earth.

In September 2016, gravitational waves were detected for the first time, by the two LIGO detectors in the USA. LIGO stands for Laser Interferometer Gravitational-Wave Observatory. Gravitational waves are "ripples in the fabric of space-time", predicted by Einstein in 1915 in his Theory of General Relativity. They are too weak to be detected unless produced by a most cataclysmic event, for example an event 1.3 billion years ago when two black holes, with masses about 29x and 36x that of our sun came closer and closer together, and in the final minutes they fused into one, releasing a huge amount of energy in a few seconds from a mass equivalent to about 3x our sun, calculated according to Einstein's equation $E=mc^2$ (where E is energy, m is mass and c is a constant equal to the speed of light).

The ability to detect and measure these gravitational waves could provide a new and powerful tool for cosmological research. Not only does it confirm Einstein's General Theory of Relativity but it also confirms a prediction made by Stephen Hawking in 1971. He realised that when two black holes collide the combined black hole they form must be bigger than the sum of its parts. In 2016, he was reported to have said "If general relativity is correct and the energy density is positive, the surface area of the event horizon—the boundary of a black hole—has the property that it always increases when additional matter or energy falls into the black hole. If two black holes collide and merge to form a single black hole, the area of the event horizon around the resulting black hole is greater than the sum of the areas of the event horizons around the original black holes."

Calculations carried out for *The Times* by Emanuele Berti at the University of Mississippi showed that the first direct measurements of black holes were a perfect fit for Professor Hawking's predictions. This is so different from theology where physical observations and calculations cannot be made.

The original announcement of the detection of gravitational waves was widely applauded but since 2016 grave doubts have been expressed about the observation of gravitational waves, which may have been nothing more than background noise in the detectors. The waves are so weak that it is very difficult to build detectors that are sensitive enough to separate signal from noise. It seems that by 2020 the detection of gravitational waves has yet to be generally accepted by international scientists.

How satisfying is the Standard Model of Cosmology as an explanation of our world? It tells us that the universe is flat, at least to within a few percent and that it is homogeneous and isotropic to one part in 100,000. It tells us something about what things happened or may have happened, but does not explain how they happened, or anything about why they should have happened. The events described and the measurements given are completely outside our imagination but of course the universe was very different at the time of the Big Bang compared with how it is now.

The fact that the universe is expanding has been known for some time, but it is only more recently that it has been discovered that it is not only expanding but expanding at an accelerating rate. This was discovered by observing distant Type 1a supernovae. These supernovae occur when a white dwarf star reaches the Chandrasekhar mass limit and explodes. By studying the observed brightness of this explosion against time (the so-called light curve), it is possible to calibrate the intrinsic luminosity of the supernova to better than 10% so it is then an object of known absolute brightness. [Cosmologists call them Standard Candles.] By measuring its apparent brightness, it is possible to calculate its distance from Earth.

Using calculations of this kind in conjunction with X-rays it has been suggested that the universe is not isotropic, after all. Observations were made in which some distant objects were less bright than the calculations indicated they should have been, when looking in one direction, but when looking in another direction distant objects looked brighter than expected. The observations may prove to be due to technical errors, but if they are substantiated it would be of the greatest theoretical importance because the idea that the universe is isotropic has been fundamental to cosmology.

The Lambda CDM model as described above is accepted by most cosmologists as provisionally correct at the time of going to press but there are aspects of the theory that make it unacceptable to some theorists. One such discontent about the theory concerns the Cosmological Constant. The evidence that the universe is expanding at an accelerating rate, based on observations of type 1a supernovae as described above, Cosmic Microwave Background measurements and detailed studies of large-scale structure are all in good agreement. All the data are consistent with Lambda CDM cosmology but provide a value for the cosmological constant which, when expressed in Planck units, is very much too small. Two questions arise: Why is the value of Lambda so small? And: Why is the energy density of this cosmological constant so close to the present matter density? One possible solution is by using the anthropic principle. A universe with a larger cosmological constant would not be able to support the formation of large-scale structures and the presence of life capable of asking why the cosmological constant is so small. This suggests that the laws of physics allow for a large number of universes as envisaged by string theory. The enormous number of compactifications of string theory down to four dimensions would result in a wide variety of de Sitter vacua, each having a different value for the cosmological constant, but so far there has not been a satisfactory way found to fit de Sitter space into string theory. The cosmological constant should not be so small, because known particles, such as electrons, should be contributing to it and this is something difficult to explain.

This is a very complex and intellectually demanding subject. It is leading to what is called *new physics*, as studies lead to possible extensions of the Lambda CDM model and to what is known as *modified gravity.* These subjects are way beyond the scope of this book but they are mentioned here to once again underline the fact that although science has given us great advances in many practical aspects of life, our knowledge of how the world works is still limited, conditional and uncertain.

It is the very first second of the Lambda CDM theory that is the most controversial: did the process start from a singularity—an infinitesimally small size and amazingly high temperature and pressure? The reasoning behind the idea of the singularity is that we see that the universe is getting larger all the time and getting cooler. Going backwards in time the universe used to be smaller and hotter. Going back a very long time (13.7 billion years) the extrapolation takes one to the singularity. But some cosmologists suggest that although the early universe was very small and very hot it never went back to being as small as a singularity. Instead they believe that the starting point was that space contained no matter or radiation, but that it did contain energy. This vacuum energy was what provided the conditions for the initiation of the processes that constitute the Lambda CDM model. So it is postulated that the first thing was not the Big Bang, but the existence of space containing only energy and that the Big Bang happened at some time after that.

At the present time, it is thought by some cosmologists that parts of our Universe are expanding more quickly than other parts but that these areas are separate from one another and do not interfere with each other.

Of course what happened before the Big Bang is very speculative indeed. Anything before that has probably left nothing that can be observed now. Despite that, there are many theories about what might have happened before the Big Bang and much thought given to what evidence there *could* be remaining from then.

One theory is that there was a previous universe that expanded for a very long time and then began to contract. It continued to contract until it became a singularity and the Big Bang occurred. According to this theory, the universe might have gone through many such cycles, each one lasting perhaps a trillion years.

There are some ideas in science that are so far from every day experience that it is not possible for people to visualise them. Quantum mechanics and the Heisenberg uncertainty principle show the difficulty of being precise about the properties of matter at any given moment. Leonard Susskind, who was one of the principals in the foundation of String Theory, has more recently developed the principle of black hole complementarity. This means that there is ambiguity about what happens to an object that enters a black hole. An outside observer would think that the object was destroyed as it reaches the event horizon (perimeter) of the black hole, but to the object itself this would not happen until it reached the hole's centre (singularity). Both descriptions are equally valid. Around 1995 Susskind and Gerard 'tHooft formulated what they called the holographic principle. (A holograph is a two-dimensional picture of something which contains within it all the information needed to make a three-dimensional image.) This states that what happens in any volume of space-time can be explained by what happens on its boundary. This means that objects could equally well be traveling in three-dimensional space, as we feel that we are, or be flattened blobs traveling on a two-dimensional surface. Not something that we can imagine or comprehend.

The universe that we can see is much less than the total that exists. String theory leads on to the multiverse theory: that there are large numbers of universes, in addition to our own. Stephen Hawkins believed strongly in this theory, and has stated that there may be as many as 10^{500} of them. That does take some believing, as a googol (10^{100}) is already a larger number than anything that could be counted, such as the number of atoms in the universe. So it seems that present day theoretical physics is going way beyond what people are capable of imagining.

An unusual planet was discovered in 2011, which is 4,000 light years from Earth. This planet orbits a star of a type known as a pulsar. The pulsar (named PSRJ1719-1438) is very remarkable, because it is only 12 miles (19.3 Km) in diameter, but it contains more matter than our sun. (1.4 times the mass of the sun, which is about 10^{15} times larger) so it is unimaginably dense. It spins on its axis 10,000 times a minute, which would be expected to cause its disintegration under the huge force produced by the rotation, but it's very high density holds it together. The planet that orbits around it is large, with a diameter of 40,000 miles (64,373 Km), compared to Earth with a diameter of about 7,500 miles (12,070 Km). Despite this large size, it orbits the star in only 130 minutes. Perhaps the most remarkable thing about this planet is that it is thought to be made almost entirely of diamond. If enough pressure is applied to pure carbon at a high enough temperature, it will form diamond. It is not known what this planet would look like as it is too far away to see: it has been detected using radio telescopes in Australia and England. It may be made of diamond covered with a black layer of carbon. Objects like this pulsar and its planet are real. They exist in our own galaxy, yet they are so different from our own solar system that they are completely outside our own experience of the physical world.

Reality

There is a perception that science can describe objective reality, but this is not as strongly held by scientists now. In the 19th century, it was probably a widely held view, but by the middle of the 20th century ideas had changed. Although Albert Einstein thought that science should seek to provide the basis for a mental picture of what reality is, other scientists of that time, such as the leading physicist Niels Bohr, thought that it was dangerous to be too dogmatic about this: scientists should confine themselves to making observations and measurements.

This brings us to consider what is reality? So much has been written about this by philosophers over the centuries. It is a vast subject outside the scope of this book but some important philosophical ideas about the nature of reality have already been discussed in this chapter, in the section on Critical Realism, above. There are the opposing views of modernity which depends heavily on empirical observations to assert certainty over reality, contrasted with post-modernity which denies that reality can be defined or detected. This becomes a problem when attempting to define the whole of reality at the same time and with one set of methods. It seems to me that the difficulties with these opposing views largely evaporate if one considers physical reality separately from spiritual reality. We are entitled to expect that the physical world can be observed and measured, but we cannot expect that of the spiritual world. The physical and spiritual worlds should be examined separately, using methods appropriate to the respective subjects, after which the results of both sets of studies may be compared. The fact that we cannot weigh and measure goodness and beauty does not make them any less real.

The philosopher Gabriel Marcel (1889–1973) argued that events could be divided into two separate and distinct categories which he called Problems and Mysteries. He said that problems were things that one could attempt to solve and having solved them, they lost much of their interest. But mysteries were things that one could think about for a long time without coming to any firm conclusions. The more one thought about them, the more mysterious and interesting they became. That seems to be a very sensible view: problems are the subject of scientific inquiries but mysteries are in the province of philosophy and theology. Problems can be solved by the application of practical common sense and science; a problem could be solved by one person or another. Once solved, the solution is available to everybody. A person can be deeply concerned about a problem, but it remains essentially outside themselves. But a mystery is very intimately connected within themselves, it is part of their being.

There is now a perception that reality is stratified; an object can be differently described depending on whether it is being described by a chemist or physicist or by an artist, poet, philosopher or theologian: different ways of looking at the same thing.

For our purposes perhaps the practical, every day way to define reality is that it is what appears real to the observer. But how do we know if one observer is seeing something the same way as another? A certain wavelength of visible light produces a certain colour, named in an arbitrary way, but recognised by everyone. So the colour blue (4240 to 4912 Angstroms) is seen by people, associated with the colour of the sea and the sky on a sunny day. But it is not possible to be sure that everyone sees blue in exactly the same way, although the fact that most people would agree about what are pleasing or displeasing combinations of colour suggests that we do all see the colours similarly.

What a person thinks about the world is what is real to them. It may be that a more scientific definition of reality is not possible, or even desirable. Considerations such as these make it increasingly clear that the natural world cannot be exactly characterised by science, or perhaps it would be better to say that an exact characterisation by science can leave the reader with no concept of what the "object" is *"really"* like. It seems to me that the concept of reality—what something *really* is—has to be linked to the scale of magnitude that is being discussed. If a person is sitting on a chair by a table on which there is a glass half full of water, all these objects are real to them. They are real. It does not matter that they are really made of atoms with space between them such that the objects are made of mainly empty space. That is reality at a different scale of magnitude, at the atomic level. But it could then be pointed out that the atoms themselves are composed of sub-units: protons, neutrons and electrons. But the atoms are real at their own level. The protons themselves are also composed of sub-units and it is here that it begins to get difficult to know what to call reality. What does a Quark look like? Meaningless question because it cannot look like anything. It does not have attributes that can give rise to visual images.

This situation is now complicated by the realisation that there is dark matter and dark energy in our universe. According to NASA, material of the type that we are made of, consisting of atoms (which is called baryonic matter) only makes up about 4.9% of the total mass/energy of the universe. There is also thought to be 26.8% cold dark matter and 68.3% dark energy. Dark matter does not emit or absorb radiation. It is likely to be composed of weakly interactive massive particles, but this is not known yet. It is likely to be non-baryonic, that is not made of atoms. The presence of dark matter can be inferred by the lens effect, due to the way in which light curves when it passes a massive object. Dark energy, which forms the bulk of the universe is even more mysterious. Its existence is based on theoretical physics but so far it has not been detected. So, a great deal is known, but we are far from understanding what is physical reality.

Nineteenth century

Set against this kind of information it is astonishing to read *"Vestiges"* and see how little was known about the physical world in the mid-nineteenth century. While Charles Darwin was labouring over the writing of *On Natural Selection*, a book was published anonymously in 1844 by Robert Chambers called *Vestiges of the Natural History of Creation*. (5) It was a best seller, widely read at all levels of literate society. It contains many wise words and observations, some of which would not be regarded as "politically correct" nowadays. But what is most remarkable is the insight it gives us into how little was known about the nature of the physical world at that time. Although there was a good understanding of the main features of our solar system, and there was good knowledge of geology and the laying down of different strata during the development of the Earth, there was no knowledge of sub-atomic physics, and chemistry was quite rudimentary. Biology and medicine were generally understood only at the macroscopic level and nothing was known about genetics. The book contains some remarkable misconceptions about the nature of the biological world. Chambers gave some support to the Quinarian system of classification of animals, which was based on assigning organisms to certain circles, each containing five different types, at each level of complexity. This had a brief popularity but was soon shown to be false. He also gave credence to the possibility of spontaneous generation, quoting extensively from the work of two gentlemen (Mr Crosse and Mr Weekes) who had conducted experiments in which electricity from a voltaic cell was passed through various solutions, and after a time "insects" emerged from these solutions. It was claimed that life had been produced therein, without any pre-existing ova. *Vestiges* demonstrates the working of a great intelligence, striving to understand our world, but hampered by lack of information, and sometimes by misinformation. But Chambers was able to stand back and look at the natural world and see that it was characterised by the principle of "development", that is the gradual development of more and more complex and advanced organisms over a long period of time. He elaborated his theory of development in the *Vestiges*. This was really the precursor to the work of Charles Darwin on Natural

Selection, as described in the chapter on Evolution. The word "Development" is a better one to use than "Evolution" because development implies a progressive improvement, which has happened, whereas evolution only means change, which could be for better or worse. It is for consideration why there has been progressive improvement and increasing complexity. Natural Selection might have produced some adaptations to changed environment and later changed back as the environment changed again. The mutations thought to be needed to make a plant or animal better fitted to its new environment might never have occurred. It is remarkable that they did.

Imperfections and suffering

Returning to Paley, he and many others have been worried about the "imperfections" in the world, and wondered how a loving God could make a world which contained deformities and diseases. These ideas have been used to argue against a creator, designer God. For example, Richard Dawkins points to the recurrent laryngeal nerve (which leaves the brain stem, travels down the neck, enters the thorax, loops round the aorta and travels back up the neck to the larynx) as evidence that the world was not created by a designer. But a designer of a mechanism is mainly concerned about its functionality: how well it performs. The recurrent laryngeal nerve does no harm and functions perfectly well, so there was no pressure on a designer (or Natural Selection) to change its course.

Gottfried Wilhelm Leibniz (1646–1716) was a rationalist philosopher widely regarded as one of the greatest thinkers of the modern world. He conceived the ideas of differential and integral calculus independently of Isaac Newton who was working on the same ideas at the same time. As well as mathematics he wrote about many other subjects including physics and theology. He said that it was inconceivable that an all-powerful God would deliberately allow the creation of a Universe that was not as good as it could have been. Therefore the world we live in is *The best of all possible worlds*". This did not mean that there was no sin or suffering in the world but that there could not be a world with less. He also made the observation that we only see and know about a tiny fraction of the Universe. It is rather like looking at one small corner of a picture; which does not tell one much about the rest of the picture. So we should not be too critical of the Universe for its imperfections because most of it may be free of sin and suffering. Now we do know so much more about the vastness of the Universe and its composition and it is very likely that sin and suffering only occur on this planet Earth, which is a very minute fraction of the whole Universe.

Concerns about the imperfections of the world and the consequent suffering this produces are usually answered in relation to the "free will" that we are given. Although the natural world follows fundamental laws, people are not robots tied rigidly to one form of expression. We have choice, and choice is evident throughout the natural world.

It would not be right for God to prevent some natural disaster, for example by stopping a volcano erupting, because that would mean that he had to interfere with the laws of physics. If God frequently interfered with the laws of physics, we would never have been able to discern them. But there are good reasons to believe that God does act in other ways to modify events. This may be done by affecting the time at which things happen, such as precisely the time at which a person comes across another person who is in need of help. A few seconds earlier or later and the need might not have been recognised. God might also act to affect the way in which a person is thinking, to modify their response to a particular challenge. God is not a physical being and therefore generally acts in spiritual rather than material ways.

Suffering is an inevitable consequence of being a physical entity which is bound to age, wear out and go wrong. It is only when people are spirits, free of their physical body, that they will have the possibility of freedom from suffering, if that is God's will for them. Do not bank on it. No one knows what the pass mark is to get into heaven. It is thought that God's will would be for everyone to go to heaven, but it has to be only those who love God and put God first in their lives at all times. It may be that the great majority of us fail this test, including me. At present, God is listening to about seven billion people, and perhaps one day God's word will have spread to everyone and everyone will be loving God and loving the people around them, so that they will all be worthy of Heaven. The qualities most needed to strive for are unselfishness and humility. "The meek shall inherit the Earth." But meekness does not mean weakness, on the contrary it is strength: to recognise one's shortcomings, to know one cannot always be self-sufficient, that one needs God to forgive and help one, and one needs to reach out to other people and put them first.

It must be remembered that at this time in which we are living much suffering is caused by the selfishness of people, who cause great harm to other people. Islam believes that the free will that people have, which gives us choice of action, also makes people answerable for their own actions; each person has to take responsibility for their own behaviour, and not blame God when things do not work out well. Jesus Christ gave people two duties: to love God and to love your neighbour, which completely rules out selfish behaviour. The message from the cross is the importance of unselfishness: to lay down one's life for others. Natural disasters are due to natural laws, and it would not be reasonable for God to interfere with the laws of physics because if God did intervene frequently it would be impossible to make any predictions about the natural world, and the laws of physics would have been impossible to discover.

In Paley's day, it was generally thought that God was still active in the day-to-day creation of new species, but this idea was soundly disputed in *Vestiges*. If that had been true, it would have put full responsibility on God for the deformities, diseases and parasitism that distress so many. In fact, some churchmen of the day welcomed the way in which Natural Selection removed that responsibility from God. Nowadays it is generally supposed that God acted initially to set up or *allow* the universe, and this included laws that would continue to govern natural processes without detailed supervision or interference. That could be consistent with micro-evolution, but the large changes of macro-evolution may well have been the result of direct action by God.

There are some "critical control points" at which it is likely that God did have to act: the Big Bang, the creation of life and the making of people from a primitive human. But more than that, there are reasons to suppose, as we will see in later chapters, that evolution by Natural Selection would not have worked very well, or quickly enough, unless there is some form of guiding force to point evolution in a certain developmental direction. This would not have been needed if there was inheritance of acquired characteristics, and Darwin put a lot of emphasis on the importance of this. He devised an ingenious hypothetical mechanism by which it might work, which he named "Pangenesis", which he defended strongly. It is now known that the genetic inheritance of acquired characteristics is not possible. Bear in mind that the gametes (ova and sperm) carried in the bodies of women and men of reproductive age were fully defined genetically before they were born, in the second trimester of their mother's pregnancy. Their gametes were formed before they had experienced any independent life, so any acquired characteristics, such as the farrier's strong arms, arose long after the formation of the genes that would be passed on to the farrier's children. There is now thought to be some epigenetic inheritance which is not mediated through genes but at present this is thought likely to be of relatively minor importance compared with genetic inheritance. The absence of inheritance of acquired characteristics greatly weakens the effectiveness of Natural Selection as a developmental influence.

Returning to the question of suffering, much of the suffering in the world is due to the presence of evil, as personified by Satan. It is he who causes the suffering, not God. This is an argument which does not seem to be brought forward much nowadays in discussions of religion and science in relation to suffering. It has been observed that Satan has been clever in hiding himself from view, so that even many religious people no longer believe in him, despite clear references to Satan in the Bible (Old Testament: Job, New Testament: the Gospels) This gives greater opportunities for Satan to do unsuspected harm and to promote evil opaquely.

Is Satan a real being, or is the name really a personalisation of the whole gamut of evil influences that exist, mostly derived from our inherited animal instinct of selfishness? It would be foolhardy to suggest that Satan does not exist, but at the same time there is only one God, so Satan must be some form of spiritual being, permitted by God but infinitely inferior to God. That would fit with the book of Job which describes Satan talking to God about doing harm to Job. There is a lot of evidence pointing to the existence and activities of evil spirits and some examples are described later in this book.

It is important not to blame God for the evil actions of people, under the influence of Satan. Anyone who has experienced the actions of evil spirits will need no convincing about the reality of the spirit world and supernatural events. It seems to be true that supernatural events caused by God, that is to say miracles, are rare events. That must be so, because if God frequently over-ruled natural laws, we would be left in a state of uncertainty and confusion: nothing would be predictable. But Satan has no such concerns and poltergeist activity is known to be quite commonplace. An excellent Biblical exegesis of evil spirits is given by Peter Horrobin in his book *Healing Through Deliverance* (6). Of course, science has no role in the understanding of supernatural events, because it does not have any tools to detect them. People who have not experienced these things often disbelieve the people who have experienced them, dismissing them as deluded or fraudulent. Such dismissal is resented, especially when it comes from scientists. It is wrong to dismiss something as imaginary just because you have not experienced it yourself: the first rule of science is to approach the unknown with an unbiased mind and not to jump to foregone conclusions. Some people might disbelieve the powerful twisting of a willow wand used for water divining when it is near water, but once one has experienced this, as I have, it cannot be denied, as will be described in a later chapter.

The suffering we have to endure is an inevitable consequence of natural disasters, our decaying physical world and the selfishness within ourselves and those around us.

Science

Science is at its best when it demonstrates simple physical laws which have mathematical constancy. For example, there is a common physics experiment done in schools, in which an iron rod is heated and its length is measured at different temperatures. It is found that the rod gets longer as the temperature increases. It is then possible to draw a graph of temperature against length and demonstrate a mathematical relationship between them. (Of course that leaves the question "What makes the rod get longer?" and the answer to that is that the greater energy given to the atoms makes it get longer, but that is a superficial answer and a more detailed explanation would depend on detailed understanding of atomic physics.) This exemplifies the three aspects of science: observation, measurement and calculation. Unless a scientific theory is backed up by supporting physical observations, measurements and mathematical formulae it cannot be accepted. Unfortunately there is a lot of "scientific" work which does not satisfy these criteria, and cannot properly be called science. Much that is done in sociology and in biology, including medicine, is poorly controlled, but is passed off as science. Observations are made and conclusions drawn which are often intuitive rather than strictly scientific. They are not always backed by rigorous mathematical (statistical) analysis. Much work is published in clinical pharmacology that is not based on randomised, double-blind, placebo-controlled trials. Such work can be useful. It is sometimes the best that can be done in areas where measurements are difficult, or the thing being measured is not precise, such as in psychometric studies. But these quasi-scientific observations should be recognised for what they are, and not be elevated to the status of truly scientific results.

Some of the most speculative areas of science are in anthropology. Ian Tattersall, a curator in the Division of Anthropology at the American Museum of

Natural History, retains a high level of objectivity. He has written several highly regarded books on anthropology. In *The world from beginnings to 4000 BCE* (7) he wrote "The problem has been that palaeoanthropologists have tended to dive in at the deep end, going directly to full-fledged scenarios. This has tended to reduce discussion in this field to a sort of storytelling competition." Much has been written about our hominid ancestors, but it is nearly all conjecture: even species designations, based on a few bone fragments, are probably very unreliable. If it is true that Neanderthals interbred with *Homo sapiens* they could not have been a separate species, probably a sub-species.

The British Museum presented a beautiful and interesting exhibition in the spring of 2013, called "Ice age art". It presented a number of sculptures and carvings (mostly only two or three inches—50mm to 75mm—in size) dating back to about 35,000 years ago. It was regrettable that this had the sub-title "Arrival of the modern mind". A beautifully presented and written book accompanied the exhibition (8). The introduction to the book stated "Identifying the arrival of the modern brain [*sic*] in Europe through the oldest known art works is an important aspect of the exhibition." (N.B. The modern *brain* is not thought to be significantly different from the brain of 100,000 years ago.) But Henry Moore was used as an example of the modern mind. Surely he it was who tended to go back to more simplistic and primitive forms. A better example of the modern mind in sculpture might have been Auguste Rodin or Michelangelo. We simply do not know the significance of works of art from twenty or thirty thousand years ago. The beautiful cave paintings of the period, found principally in France and nearby countries, are highly unusual and atypical of the general level of activity and mental expression of that time.

There may be a place for speculation, which is a powerful desire in some people, but it must be seen for what it is. One good thing about real science is that it limits its own area of activity. If it cannot be observed and measured, it cannot be verified and therefore is not science.

Religion

Religion does not have that rigorous self-limiting nature. Over thousands of years people have struggled to understand the nature of God, and how God interacts with people. It is not surprising that many different interpretations have emerged over the millennia. In recent centuries, the three great monotheistic religions have come close to harmony in the broad outlines of belief and ethics, although there are very important differences between them.

Christians believe in one God. Most Christians believe in the Unity of the Trinity: the Triune God, consisting of three "persons", the Father, the Son and the Holy Ghost. There are also Unitarian Christians who do not accept the doctrine of the Trinity. Charles Darwin's wife Emma was a Unitarian.

Islam is grounded in the rigid belief that there is only one God who cannot be divided in any way. That is the main reason for conflict between Muslims and Christians.

The Jewish religion was founded by Abraham on the belief that there is only one God.

There are only three possible states: no God, one God or more than one God.

Therefore, *as it is true* that there is only one God, it follows that people of all three religions are worshiping the *same* God, even though their perceptions of what God is like are not the same. There is only one God to worship. Realisation of this should reduce conflict.

Revelation, interpretation and faith are susceptible to very fluid definitions and to very variable outcomes. Religions have to be, and are, self-defining. It is generally accepted that the core beliefs and rules of a religion are established at the outset and cannot be changed later. But you might ask "What are the core beliefs?" In the Jewish tradition there are two types of laws that govern these things: apodictic law and casuistic law. These have been said to be equivalent to "principles" and "rules". So apodictic law concerns the unchanging core beliefs, for example the Decalogue (Ten Commandments) but casuistic law is more like case law, it can be modified somewhat in response to changing circumstances. But if someone wants to make a profound change to an existing religion, that means starting a new religion or at least a new branch of the old religion. Of course this happens, for example Roman Catholic, Protestant and Eastern Orthodox Christians and Sunni and Shi'ite Muslims. In this sense, all religious people are (or should be) fundamentalists. Unfortunately that word has recently become associated with people who turn to extreme violence to support their beliefs and it is regrettable when extreme harm is caused because of a difference in religious view. This happens because for many people their religion is the most important thing in life. Of course a person's relationship with God *is* the most important thing in their life. But for our present times it might be better to adopt not religious tolerance but religious toleration: thus one group may profoundly disagree with another group, but it should be prepared to tolerate them in peace, instead of slaughtering them. Let them persist in their errors, they might say.

We have just seen that the original precepts of a religion cannot be altered or watered down. But it is not possible to "prove" or "disprove" a religious principle. It is wrong to try to do so. The concepts of proof or disproof belong to science, not to religion. In fact, the concept of proof is contrary to religion, because it would eliminate the need for faith: but faith is an essential pillar of religion. Belief in God is not meant to be something that can be proved, which would mean that it required little thought and no faith. That may be one reason why God does not want his existence to be a certainty and why it is wrong to try to prove the existence of God. If God had wanted his existence to be a proven fact, he would have made that happen.

Despite that, there have been theological propositions that do seek to prove the existence of God such as that of *Leibniz* (see below).

Religion should require mental effort and a conscious act of faith. Even science does not use the concept of proof as much as the concept of disproof: a theory is accepted until it is disproved. Science is designed to test falsifiable hypotheses by gathering evidence. Religion does not do this. To reduce the world to falsifiable factual phenomena ignores the great wealth of human culture expressed in art and literature throughout the historical period, thus science is only part of the intellectual activity of a complete person.

It is sometimes said that scientists may have faith in one theory in preference to another. But it can be argued that the word "faith" should be confined to religious situations and not used in relation to science. When a scientist is confronted with two different theories that seek to explain a phenomenon, they will look at how well the theories fit the available observed evidence, and will support the theory that fits best and gives the most accurate results and predictions, knowing that in time to come it may be replaced by an alternative theory which gives better results and predictions. They have *confidence* in the theory but this is *conditional*. This is absolutely different to religious faith, which is an expression of the certainty that something is correct, without reference to any test results. It is a certainty that cannot be eroded by any new knowledge because it is based on a timeless belief, which is itself based on a divine revelation. This is sometimes referred to as "A blind leap of faith," but it is not blind because it has sturdy theological foundations. It is regarded as blind only by people who refuse to acknowledge the existence of a spiritual world and God.

There is nothing wrong with faith in a theological context, it has to be that way. Blind leaps of faith are only used by scientists when they are writing up their grant funding applications.

Theology

Theology is the study of God. One might ask: How much should one try to know about God? The important thing is to believe in God, but not to try to analyse God. It is a huge subject covering many cultures and thousands of years. Leibniz deduced that God was 'Necessary' because (a) All substances in the Universe must have an explanation. (b) The sum of all these substances means that the Universe itself must have an explanation. (c) The only possible explanation is God. This is reasonable enough, but it does not tell one that God is a loving being who cares for creation. That depends on other theological considerations. These generally lead to the conclusion that God is all-powerful and everlasting and loves the world he made and all people. That is the belief of the Abrahamic religions, but Buddhism and the Hindu religion take somewhat different views.

The founder of Buddhism, Siddhartha Gautama, who lived about 2,500 years ago, believed in individual spiritual advancement, a world of the spirit and life after death but he did not believe in a creator God. He is believed to have given three reasons, stated briefly as follows:

(1) Belief in God was only due to people wanting a powerful force to turn to in adversity: (2) The many different ideas about God and the numerous Gods that were worshipped made the concept unsupportable: (3) There was no need for a God, because science could explain everything.

The first argument is still used today. The fallacy is to suppose that someone would invent a God to comfort themselves in time of trouble. It is the other way round: it has to come from the outside to be effective. God reached out to people and made himself known to them. They responded to him in times of plenty and in times of hardship, and thus found consolation and strength from their God. At the time when the Buddha was alive, religions all worshipped numerous deities, such as the Greek and Roman pantheons, except for the Israelites who, since Abraham, had believed in one God. The Buddha may not have been aware of Abraham. There was no science in 600BC, so this may have been added later. It is not a valid argument as discussed in this book. Science has nothing to do with it.

The Hindu religion has developed over many centuries from earlier beliefs and cannot be said to have a definite starting date. Its beliefs and practices vary widely depending on the particular tradition being followed. It has complex ideas about God and the after-life. In brief, it supposes that there are many lesser Gods, who relate in some way to one Supreme Being. The belief is that every living thing has a soul, some believing that all these souls are part of the Supreme Being, with others believing that the souls are separate from the Supreme Being. Hinduism believes in reincarnation: after death a person's soul attaches to a new body. This can happen time after time, until the person lives such a holy life that they escape from this cycle and have everlasting rest.

As a very wide approximation, the Abrahamic religions (Judaism, Christianity and Islam), all believe that there is only one God (and therefore all worship the same God, although they have differing ideas about the nature of God) who is the all-powerful and eternal being who created the spiritual and material worlds. God has always existed and is reason and knowledge. They believe that God is distinct from his creation but he has love for it and has a plan for mankind. He gave people our souls, language, intellect and our immortality. He is able to deliver people from their suffering and from the consequences of their wrong-doing. God must be worshipped and asked for forgiveness, and given thanks for all good things. However this is a very great over simplification of two thousand years of Western thought concerning the nature of God. It is a vast subject that cannot be discussed more here, but there are many good sources available today which cover the many aspects of theology. Regarding Christian theology, a recent and authoritative text is the book by Andrew Wright that has been quoted from earlier in this chapter. Alistair McGrath has written many books about Christian theology. Currently his latest work is a magnificent trilogy with the title *A Scientific Theology.* (9) The three volumes are named *Nature, Reality* and *Theory.* I regret that some of what I have written in this book may appear at first sight to be contrary to McGrath, because he is such a great theologian and I am nothing of a theologian. But the explanation is that I am talking about the practical conduct of scientific work whereas he is talking about the deeply philosophical aspects which underlie science and theology. It is my contention that the practical results of observation and experimentation in the physical sciences can have no relevance as to whether or not to believe in God. This is important because of the emphasis that the New Atheists have placed on the importance of the physical sciences in support of their views, and this needs to be countered.

All five of the world's greatest religions, which represent the great majority of people living now, have in common a belief in a spiritual side to our being and the existence of a spiritual world, with some form of after-life. All except Buddhists believe in a creator God.

For the purposes of this book, there is really no need to say any more about theology. But as stated elsewhere, anyone wishing to dispute the existence or nature of God must use theological arguments, not science-based arguments, to advance their case.

Science cannot be applied to religion or theology

Unfortunately some people have tried to use "scientific" approaches to religion, for example to test whether prayer is effective in producing cures of diseases. This is the height of foolishness for several reasons. It is not easy to show even that a new vaccine is safe and effective. First it requires a lot of knowledge about the vaccine and its potency, so that large and small doses can be compared with no dose, in large groups of similar individuals under controlled conditions. How can one measure the potency of a prayer? Measuring outcomes is also difficult enough in animal studies, more difficult in human populations. To test the efficacy of anything as ill-defined as prayer is nonsense. But more importantly, it is not right to expect God to allow himself to be tested in this way. When Satan tempted Jesus, taking him to a high point on the Temple and saying that he should cast himself down, to show that God would send his angels to protect him, Jesus answered "It is written, Thou shalt not tempt the Lord thy God." (Do not put the Lord your God to the test). Joseph Ratzinger, who became Pope Benedict XV1, wrote a book called *Jesus of Nazareth*. (10) Thinking about this point, he wrote:

"We are dealing here with the vast question as to how we can and cannot know God, how we are related to God and how we can lose him. The arrogance that would make God an object and impose our laboratory conditions upon him is incapable of finding him. For it already implies that we deny God as God by placing ourselves above him, by discarding the whole dimension of love, of interior listening; by no longer acknowledging as real anything but what we can experimentally test and grasp. To think like that is to make oneself God. And to do that is to abase not only God, but the world and oneself, too."

"Interior listening" is of prime importance. It is only by talking to God and listening for that connection as God listens to us that we can have any real and personal knowledge of God. Then belief in God becomes knowledge of God. It is inevitable.

Belief in God

Ultimately, belief in God is due to the innermost thoughts and feelings of an individual, who knows within themselves that their belief is right; they experience communion with God. This is something that non-believers cannot understand because they have not experienced it themselves. It is surprising that otherwise clever and perceptive people may be unable to see that if they have not experienced God in their own being, they are not in a position to say anything about God. They also ignore the teaching of the prophets and the many great theologians from past and present times, as well as the millions of people around the world who do believe in God. In fact, many scientists do have faith in God, and do not see any conflict between their religious belief and their scientific work. Their religious belief will shape their approach to their life and their work, but the science itself is unaffected: thus the observations, measurements and calculations are unchanged by theology.

Richard Dawkins is the distinguished geneticist, until recently Professor of the Understanding of Science at Oxford, who has become very well-known because of his writing on genetics in relation to evolution and his opposition to creationists. Clearly he believes that there is almost certainly no creator God, but his opposition to belief in God may not be so much to do with that as to his view that religion has many harmful influences. He presents a convincing argument to support evolution, which he says is a fact as good as any in science. In 2009, he published a book called *The Greatest Show on Earth* (11) in which he said he made up for deficiencies in his earlier works, which did not really set out to prove the truth of evolution. It is a beautifully produced, scholarly and informative book. He deplores creationists (in the specific North American sense) who deny that evolution has taken place. He calls them history deniers, and his frustration with them is very understandable. Evolution, meaning simply development from earlier forms, is a fact that nobody need deny. To do so reduces the credibility and status of the denier. But there is no need for a devout Christian, or anyone else, to deny evolution. The correct stance for creationists is that God created everything but when Genesis was written about 3000 years ago, only a very simple account could be revealed to the writers, suitable for the understanding of the people of the time. Now we know from the material record that evolution has taken place: that is how God did it, but only up to the point of *Homo sapiens*. My divergence from Richard Dawkins is because he is a "People denier". He seems not to accept that present day people are very different from our ancestors of 100,000 years ago. In a book intended for children, he wrote "There was no first human." That is correct. But he should acknowledge that there were "First people", who appeared suddenly only some seventy thousand years ago. They became more obviously people 10,000 years ago when there was a sudden behavioural change from the hunting and gathering life style to a sedentary life style in villages, with the development of agriculture. That is also a scientific fact demonstrated by the material record.

Atheism

The Greatest Show on Earth is a convincing proof of evolution. But it contains the interesting admission that Natural Selection may not be the complete explanation for how evolution works. That is very significant, coming from Richard Dawkins. What his book does not prove is his belief that present day people are the result of unaided Natural Selection. He denies that people are different: that there was a sudden quite recent change which made us the people we are today. Dawkins ignores this, perhaps because it is too recent to be due to evolutionary or genetic changes. He has put great effort into writing scientific support for evolution, and he appears to think that this in some way supports his atheist belief: it does not, because scientific results have no relevance to theology. The whole book is a superb proof of evolution but has absolutely no relevance to belief in God. It is a scientific book, not a theological book. A religious person can read it with interest, without any need whatever to doubt their belief in God. It could indeed be taken as supportive of Natural Theology!

A prevalent attitude of atheists is also demonstrated in a book by Jared Diamond (12) called *"The world until yesterday"*. In this book, he devotes a chapter to speculate on the origins and evolution of religion. He saw this essentially as an exercise in trying to see what advantages would accrue to people through religion. But this is completely missing the point, as one might expect from someone without knowledge of God. Religion is not about the benefits to man, it is about the benefits to God. What does God get out of it? The origin and development of religion is easily explained. God revealed himself to people at various times and in various ways, notably to the five great universal profits: Abraham, Noah, Moses, Jesus and Muhammad, but also no doubt to many other unknown people. These people responded by trying their best to understand the nature of God and to develop what they thought were the right ways to relate to God. This process continued for a long time and it is not surprising that it resulted in a variety of interpretations and many different religions. But all these religions had the effect of drawing people to God, getting people talking to God. That, it must be surmised, is the purpose of having people. *The purpose of people is to talk to God.* That is the reason for our existence. That is why we were made able to talk. The only living thing that has language. It was the will of God that there should be one living being that could talk to him and to each other. That is why we were made, in his image and likeness.

A book called *Why Us* that I found much more helpful was published by James Le Fanu, in 2009 (13). It is a very interesting and well written book. The author's main concern was to counter the way in which Darwin's theory of Natural Selection, coupled with the extensive increase in knowledge of the material world, had been combined together to discredit and bury the concepts of the non-material world and the soul. Le Fanu pointed out that the Human Genome Project has mapped out the sequence of genes in the human genome but has not given the slightest insight into how the genome works. It has been surprising to find that the human genome has about 25 thousand genes, but some less complex animals have more. A simple worm may have 12 thousand genes. The genes control the manufacture of the individual components of life, the proteins and enzymes which create the structures of living things, but Le Fanu asserts that there is nothing in the double helix of DNA which can be seen to determine the nature of the complete animal. What codes for the difference between a mouse and an elephant? He also points out that the Decade of the Brain project has failed to show how the brain produces thought. It has shown the workings of the brain to be even more complex and mysterious than previously thought. The book makes a strong case for the existence of a non-material world, but Le Fanu professes no religious faith. He asks, as I do, that people should not use science for a personal obsession against religion. I would like to quote a paragraph from Le Fanu's book which expresses his view very powerfully. "So the human mind, and what it might be, is conspicuous only by its absence from the discourse of neuroscientists. Nobody has the slightest idea how anything material [such as the brain] could be conscious, observed the cognitive scientist Jerry Fodor. Nobody even knows what it would be like to have the *slightest idea* about how anything material could be conscious. And that, to put it simply, is how the combination of a progressive evolutionary doctrine and the progressive unravelling of the complexities of biology drove underground the twin pillars of the 'non-material', the formative vital force of life and the human soul. Together they successfully extinguished the challenge to their exclusive claims to knowledge by first conflating the non-material realm with religious belief rooted in the past, while simultaneously allying their exclusively materialist explanations with the Enlightenment vision of a better world. That dual nature of reality, the material and non-material, would remain buried so long as science continued to advance towards that better future. But when its remorseless progress reached its final destination, the genome of man and fly spelt out, the brain observed 'in action' smelling a rose and constructing a sentence, the reality of the non-material domain would, inevitably, re-emerge from the shadows."

Thus there are fundamental differences between science and religion, both in their methodology and in their nature: self-limiting or infinite. Therefore scientific advances can never have any religious significance. Science is largely descriptive. It tells us what things are like and sometimes tells us how they work. That is all.

The minuteness of the initial singularity before the Big Bang, its enormously high temperature and the huge increase in size in a miniscule length of time which the Standard Model proposes are so extreme and so different to our experience of the world that we cannot imagine them. The figures are so far outside our experience that they are only accepted because they are supported by science and therefore, at present, they are thought to be correct, but only conditionally. An interesting difference with theology is that it does not really matter to a person's life or death whether they have confidence in the Standard Model or not, whereas belief in God or no belief in God strongly affects their whole life and death.

Why do some people refuse to believe in God? There are many reasons for this. It may often be because they feel unable to believe in anything that is not a physical thing, made of atoms and molecules just as we are. They do not believe in any spiritual world so therefore do not believe in God. People can be influenced towards atheism by parents, friends and teachers just as they can be drawn towards theism by those around them. Another reason for atheism may be that some people are hostile to the Church and other religious organisations. This can be for many good reasons, including bigotry and violence as well as what they regard as hypocrisy when a religious person behaves badly. Some people may resent the control that is imposed on them by following the morals of a religion. They want to "do their own thing" and not be told that it is sinful. Many people have never experienced any supernatural events so do not believe in such things. Most importantly they have never prayed to God to hear them.

Atheists have used science for many years to argue against religion and belief in God, especially after Darwin published his theory of Natural Selection. Thomas Huxley was known as "Darwin's bulldog" because of the way he harried the churchmen of the time, who were very ill equipped to give him suitable answers. It is remarkable that atheists have got away with this for so long, because it is so obvious that, by definition, science has no contact with the non-material world, so can say nothing one way or the other about belief in God. The so-called New Atheism has relied heavily on the use of science to support the view that there is no God. By now, this idea is discredited by theologians and other philosophers, but it persists in popular writing. The message that science does not support atheism needs to get to a wider audience.

New atheism

The term New Atheism arose as a journalistic response to the writing on atheism mainly by four men in the early years of the twenty first century. These were Richard Dawkins, Daniel Dennett, Sam Harris and Christopher Hitchens. Of these only Dennett is a professional philosopher. They all wrote with great conviction and largely in agreement with each other. A very useful and extremely well written summary of their ideas can be read in the Internet Encyclopaedia of Philosophy, in an article by James E. Taylor (14). He said that "It is difficult to identify anything philosophically unprecedented in their positions and arguments, but the New Atheists have provoked considerable controversy with their body of work."

James Taylor further explains that the views of these writers can be combined into a theoretical background framework which contains the following elements: a metaphysical component, an epistemological component and an ethical component. He wrote "The metaphysical component is a shared central belief that there is no supernatural or divine reality of any kind. The epistemological component is their common claim that religious belief is irrational. The moral

84

component is the assumption that there is a universal and objective secular moral standard. This moral component sets them aside from other prominent historical atheists such as Nietzsche and Sartre, and it plays a pivotal role in their arguments because it is used to conclude that religion is bad in various ways, although Dennett is more reserved than the other three."

"The New Atheists make substantial use of the natural sciences in both their criticisms of theistic belief and in their proposed explanations of its origins and evolution. They draw on science for recommended alternatives to religion. They believe empirical science is the only (or at least the best) basis for genuine knowledge of the world, and they insist that a belief can be epistemically justified only if it is based on adequate evidence. Their conclusion is that science fails to show that there is a God and even supports the claim that such a being probably does not exist. What science will show about religious belief, they claim, is that this belief can be explained as a product of biological evolution. Moreover, they think that it is possible to live a satisfying non-religious life on the basis of secular morals and scientific discoveries."

There has been some support for New Atheism and much written about it that is critical. It is questioned whether the reliance on empirical science which is so fundamental to New Atheism is scientifically justified. The fallacy is to suppose that science could in some way detect the presence of an extant non-material or supernatural being.

Humanism

Some atheists are Humanists. They deny the existence of God or any supernatural or spiritual world, believing that only the physical world that can be demonstrated by the use of scientific methods is real. They believe that they can develop satisfying ethical rules that are supportive of humanity without recourse to theological concepts. They believe that the Universe has no purpose and that there is no life after death, but they believe that people can make their lives worthwhile and have purpose by leading a useful life which respects the needs of other people and helps the people around them.

Humanists are born into a world in which the morals and ethics of the great religions are already widely known and largely practiced. It is therefore hard to know whether Humanists could have come to similar conclusions on their own, had they known nothing to start with. To the extent that Humanists glorify people and see the welfare of all people as a most important aspect of life, it is a good thing. But the absence of belief in God leaves out the more important of the two duties of man: to love God and to love your neighbour.

A number of prominent people have supported Humanism in recent decades. The British philosopher Professor A C Grayling is noteworthy. He founded and was first Master of the New College of the Humanities in London in 2011.

Scientific and theological writing

Scientific writing attempts to present a literal report of observations and measurements and is read that way. But religions are based on Holy texts and these have to be read in a religious, not a scientific way. Since the Middle Ages biblical texts have been read according to the "fourfold method of interpretation". Other texts of a religious nature, such as the 14th century alliterative poem *Piers Plowman*, by William Langland (1332–1386) can also be read by the fourfold method. This was defined by Saint Thomas Aquinas (1225–1274) in his *Summa Theologiae*. Each passage of sacred scripture has to be thought of using four different aspects at the same time. These are the literal and the spiritual, with the spiritual subdivided into allegorical, tropological and anagogical. The literal meaning of a text is the historical, factual meaning of the words. Within the spiritual meaning, allegorical signifies a sustained metaphor. Tropological deals with the moral effect of the words on the believer themselves. Anagogical signifies consideration of the final sense, the four last things: death, judgement, Heaven and Hell. Not all verses in the Bible have all of these meanings. It is said that there is nothing that is necessary for faith, which is given in a spiritual sense, which is not also given elsewhere in the Bible in the literal sense.

Up-to-date guidance on exegesis is given to us by Pope Benedict XV1 in the introduction to the second volume of his book Jesus of Nazareth. He states that there must be a balance between the hermeneutics (method of understanding texts) of the historical-critical method and the hermeneutics of theology. Both have to be deployed together to obtain a full understanding of the texts. The historical-critical method can yield important insights but must be interpreted in the light of theology. This is especially important because a wholly historical approach can lead to a view which wrongly places the events *and* the theology in the past. The historical approach has to be combined with the theological, with faith that these words of scripture emanate from the living God: they are grounded in past events but are constantly relevant and contemporary. They apply to us now, today, and will always be true.

Of course, over the past two thousand years a great many books have been written, by a great many people, bearing on various aspects of Christianity, Islam and other religions. Religious commentaries are different from scientific text books. Religious commentaries are in a sense timeless: an ancient work or a modern work can be read and compared and the ideas expressed can be related to one another usefully in a work of exegesis. But a scientific text book can become out of date quickly, with the publication of new work that needs to be fully considered in order to maintain the accuracy and relevance of the text. This emphasises the fundamental difference between theology and science. Theological ideas cannot be subject to experimental proof/disproof. Thus they remain unchanged by lack of *evidence* for change. But scientific texts are updated as new information is gathered from later experiments, observations, measurements and calculations.

It is important that religious leaders do not give in to the idea that science can have a bearing on religion/theology. Most people who become priests are unlikely to have a science-based education. Bishops are usually classical scholars and may be reluctant to speak about science if they know little about it. The name Theological Science refers to the philosophical ideas which support science and theology but in my view cannot apply to the practice of science or theology. It rather blurs the distinction between science and theology, giving atheists a toe hold that they should not have. Because of that, it might be useful for priests to be taught some of the principles of science, to help them counter the atheists' scientific arguments by showing that they are irrelevant to theology.

Unfortunately some scientists who know little about theology are not inhibited about airing their views on religious subjects although they would never think of making comment on science outside their own field of expertise. It is important, too, that men or women of religion do not make pronouncements on science without verifying that their statements are scientifically correct.

In the discussions which follow we will try to keep the clear distinctions between the practice of science and religion/theology firmly in mind. This is so even though at the sub-atomic level it may not be possible, currently, to make observations and measurements of some entities. Theological science is a deeply philosophical subject that is concerned with questions about the acquisition of true knowledge and the nature of reality. It is of value in its own field to have discussion between theologians and philosophers. In this book, it is argued that science and theology are different at the *practical* level, because of the absence of measurements, tests and mathematics in theology. This is important because atheists frequently try to use science wrongly to support their disbelief in God.

Science deals only with the material world, which it seeks to understand by observation and experiment. Theology acknowledges the material world made by God, but has no interest in investigating how it functions. It is concerned with God and with the non-material world of the spirit, which is undetectable by science.

References

1. Wright, A. (2013) *Christianity and critical realism*, London: Routledge.
2. Torrance, T. F. (1962) *Theological Science*, New York: Oxford University Press.
3. Paley, W. (1809) *Natural Theology: or Evidences of the existence and attributes of the deity, collected from the appearances of nature, 12th Edition*, London: Printed for J Faulder. See also *http://www.darwin-online.org.uk* for complete text.
4. Darwin, C. (1859) *On the origin of species by natural selection*, London: John Murray.
5. Anon (1844) *Vestiges of natural creation*, London: (Robert Chambers) John Spriggs Morss Churchill.
6. Horrobin, P. (2003) *Healing through deliverance*, Tonbridge: Sovereign World.
7. Tattersall, I. (2008) *The world from Beginnings to 4000 BCE*, Oxford University Press.
8. Cook, J. (2013) *Ice age art: the arrival of the modern mind*, British Museum Press.
9. McGrath, A. E. (2003) *A scientific theology*, London and New York and Louisville Kentucky: T & T Clark Ltd.
10. Ratzinger Joseph. Pope Benedict XV1 (2007) *Jesus of Nazareth*, London: Bloomsbury Publishing.
11. Dawkins, R. (2009) *The greatest show on earth*, London: Bantam Press. Transworld Publishers.
12. Diamond, J. (2012) *The world until yesterday*, London: Allen Lane.

13. Le Fanu (2009) *Why Us?* London: Harper Collins.
14. Taylor, J. E. *The New Atheists*, in Internet Encyclopaedia of Philosophy www.iep.utm.edu taylor@westmont.edu.

2. Evolution

The word evolution is given several meanings in the Oxford English Dictionary. The original Latin was taken to signify an unrolling, as of a written scroll. Meanings given in the OED include unrolling; opening out; disengaging from within an envelope; the appearance in orderly succession of a long train of events; in animals and plants or their parts—the process of developing from a rudimentary to a mature or complete state. A definition of biological evolution was proposed by T. H. Huxley: "The origination of living things by development from earlier forms, not by special creation." He did not need the last four words, but he wanted to make the point that he did not believe in God. As scientists now understand the word, evolution means the process through which life arose from non-living matter and subsequently developed increasing complexity. A modern definition of evolution is "Evolution is a process that results in changes in the genetic material of a population over time." Until about 150 years ago it was thought that all the plants and animals with which we are familiar were created specially and individually by God: it was not supposed that God had developed them from previously existing progenitors.

This idea was modified by Robert Chambers in his book "*Vestiges of the Natural History of Creation*" (1) He wrote so beautifully on this subject that it seems appropriate to reproduce it here. (Page 152 *et seq.*)

"A candid consideration of all these circumstances can scarcely fail to introduce into our minds a somewhat different idea of organic creation from what has hitherto been generally entertained. That God created animated beings, as well as the terraqueous theatre of their being, is a fact so powerfully evidenced, and so universally received, that I for one take it as granted. But in the particulars of this so highly supported idea, we surely here see cause for some re-consideration. It may now be inquired—In what way was the creation of animated beings effected? The ordinary notion may, I think, be not unjustly described as this—that the Almighty author produced the progenitors of all existing species by some sort of personal or immediate exertion. But how does this notion comport with what we have seen of the gradual advance of species, from the humblest to the highest? How can we suppose an immediate exertion of this creative power at one time to produce zoophytes, another time to add a few marine molluscs, another to bring in one or two conchifers, again to produce crustaceous fishes, again perfect fishes, and so on to the end? This would surely be to take a very mean view of the Creative Power—to, in short, anthropomorphise it, or reduce it to some such character as that borne by the ordinary proceedings of mankind. And yet this would be unavoidable; for that the organic creation was thus progressive through a long space of time, rests on evidence which nothing can overturn or gainsay. Some other idea must then be come to with regard to *the mode* in which the Divine Author proceeded in the organic creation. Let us seek in the history of the earth's formation for a new suggestion on this point. We have seen powerful evidence, that the construction of this globe and its associates, and inferentially that of all the other globes of space, was the result, not of any immediate or personal exertion on the part of the Deity, but of natural laws which are expressions of his will. What is to hinder our supposing that the organic creation is also a result of natural laws, which are in like manner an expression of his will? More than this, the fact of the cosmical arrangements being an effect of natural law, is a powerful argument for the organic arrangements being so likewise, for how can we suppose that the august Being who brought all these countless worlds into form by the simple establishment of a natural principle flowing from his mind, was to interfere personally and specially on every occasion when a new shell-fish or reptile was to be ushered into existence on *one* of these worlds? Surely this idea is too ridiculous to be for a moment entertained." (Emphasis in original)

(N.B. He thought that other worlds were populated with living beings.)

In Chambers' day, it was not known how old the Earth was, nor for how long there had been living creatures. It was thought that what we see now was made as it is now, not so very long ago. This was based on the first book of Genesis, which was compiled about 3000 years ago. It was an account of creation suitable for the understanding of the people of that time. Special Creation was a perfectly understandable belief, because evolution is not experienced in a person's lifetime, or even in several generations. It is much too slow a process, which can usually only be detected by comparisons of ancient fossils. In fact, there has been no noticeable evolution in the main animals and plants that we are familiar with, such as wolves and oak trees, over the past 10,000 years, or even the past 100,000 years.

It was Erasmus Darwin, an English physician (1731–1782), who was a grandfather of Charles Darwin (1809–1882), who is usually credited with first thinking about the possibility of animals and plants developing over time to reach their present form. However, a number of other thinkers had also touched upon this subject over many years, as very interestingly and enjoyably described in a book by Rebecca Stott called Darwin's Ghosts (2). Erasmus Darwin (an expressive portrait of whom hangs at the Royal Society of Medicine, London) anticipated both the work of his own grandson and also the ideas of the French biologist, Jean-Baptiste Lamarck (1744–1829). Lamarck developed his theories over a period of about ten years, and then published his *Philosophie Zoologique* in 1809. He proposed that changes in the environment caused animals to alter their behaviour, leading to some organs being better developed and others less developed, depending on need. He proposed two Laws. Lamarck's First Law was that greater use of an organ led to its increase in size and that lesser use of an organ led to a decrease in size. His Second Law was that these changes were heritable, that is, they were passed to the next generation. Lamarck did not believe in immutable (unchanging) species and tried to explain their transformation and the evolution of the animal world in terms of their response to environmental factors. He deserves more credit for these ideas than he ever received, despite the fact that the inheritance of acquired characteristics does not happen. His thoughts were very similar to those of Erasmus Darwin, although it seems that the two men did not know of each other's work. However, Lamarck's proposal that acquired characteristics can be inherited was shown to be untrue soon after that time, and this tended to discredit his other ideas. Of course in those days the mechanism of inheritance was not known and would remain obscure for another 100 years.

It was Gregor Mendel (1822–1884), an Augustinian monk, who was a biologist and botanist, who first showed how characteristics are inherited. He lived at the monastery in Brunn, Moravia, which at that time was ruled by the Austrian emperors. It is now known as Brno in the Czech Republic. He worked for over seven years (1856–1863) growing peas (*Pisum sativum*) and carrying out painstaking plant breeding experiments. He used one Tall strain of pea that grew to about six feet tall (2m) and a Dwarf strain that only grew to about one foot tall (0.33m) so they were easily distinguishable. During these years he grew over 28,000 plants. He made careful records of his experiments and recorded each plant's height, pod shape, flower location and colour and its seed shape and colour. From this work he deduced two postulates and two Laws. The postulates were (1) that inheritance was dependent on paired factors and (2) that some factors were dominant. Mendel's first Law was the Law of Segregation (or Law of Purity of Gametes). His second Law was the Law of Independent Assortment. Together these define the principles on which the inheritance of characteristics during reproduction depend. During reproduction a diploid cell containing two copies of each gene is reduced to a haploid cell (gamete) containing one copy of each gene by a process of cell division called meiosis. At conception the two haploid gametes combine together to make a diploid cell which has the potential to make all the different cell types found in the adult. The genes are independent units not affected by other genes and they are redistributed independently of one another. [But subject to Linkage discovered later.] Some genes are *dominant*: if a characteristic is present it will be represented by a dominant gene and if not present that indicates a *recessive* gene. Mendel's work was a superb intellectual achievement but it lay undiscovered until the beginning of the twentieth century. Mendel had published his work as a paper titled "Experiments on Plant Hybridisation" in the Proceedings of the Nature Research Society of Brunn, in 1866. He sent reprints of the article to 40 leading biologists around Europe, including Charles Darwin. Darwin's copy was found later, with its double pages still uncut, indicating that it had not been read. Most of the other copies were also unread, only one recipient troubling to reply. This must have been so disappointing to Mendel and it is sad that he died without knowing that within 50 years his work would be universally admired and that his name would be one of the most famous in biology. The original paper was written in German, which may partly explain why it had not been more widely read. An English translation was published in the Journal of the Royal Horticultural Society in 1901. Mendel's work then became the foundation for modern genetics when his findings were confirmed independently by the botanists Hugo de Vries and Carl Correns.

The study of biology had been given a great stimulus by the work of Carl von Linne, also known as Linnaeus (1707–1778) the Swedish naturalist and physician who founded the binomial system of nomenclature. He published his system of botanical nomenclature in *Systema Naturae* in 1735 and introduced his binomial system in 1749. In this system each individual is allocated to a species and the species are placed in a higher group called a Genus, for example, the English oak is named *Quercus* (Genus) *robur* (Species). Note that the *Genus* and *species* are always italicised in print and that the species name should never be capitalised, a common mistake in popular writing. The genera are placed in higher groupings of Families, Orders and Classes. His work was an amazing achievement which had a profound effect on his contemporaries and fully justified the epitaph on his tombstone *"Deus creavit, Linnaeus disposuit."* [God created, Linnaeus classified.]

Around the beginning of the nineteenth century there was a great upsurge of interest in biology and geology. A number of gentlemen with the time to devote to learning made great contributions to knowledge of these subjects. For example, Sir Charles Lyell (1797–1875) published his *Principles of Geology* (1830/1833) which strongly influenced contemporary scientific thought. He later published *The Geological Evidences for the Antiquity of Man*, in 1873 (3). Another influential contemporary was Sir Joseph Dalton Hooker (1817–1911). He was a leading botanist of his day, succeeding his father as Director of the Royal Botanic Gardens at Kew in 1865. These and many more led to an immense increase in scientific knowledge. Both Lyell and Hooker strongly influenced Charles Darwin.

Robert Chambers (whose family published the Chamber's Encyclopaedia) published his Hypothesis of Development 15 years before Charles Darwin published *On the Origin of Species.*

It was against this background that Charles Darwin joined a British Royal Navy survey of South American coastal waters (1831–1836) as the naturalist on board HMS Beagle. It was usually the ship's surgeon who was the naturalist on board, and there was some friction between Darwin and the ship's surgeon, who resented Darwin's appointment and the respect that he was given by the crew. Darwin worked very hard on the long voyage and returned home with a great collection of specimens and detailed notes of the observations that he had made. It was thinking about this great variety of living animals and plants, and especially about how some seemed limited to quite small areas whereas others were widely dispersed, that made him wonder about some kind of evolutionary process.

At the same time another great British naturalist, Alfred Russell Wallace (1823–1913), was also making expeditions to the Amazon basin and to the Malay

Archipelago and returning with large collections of specimens and copious notes about the observations he had made.

Most educated people have heard of Charles Darwin but few have heard of Alfred Russell Wallace, although they were contemporaries, they were both dedicated and gifted naturalists and they both independently thought out the theory of Natural Selection.

Wallace was a man of great courage and fortitude. He made long visits to both the Amazon and to the Malay Archipelago in search of specimens. He suffered badly from dreadful tropical disease as well as many deprivations due to frequently living in the most uncomfortable conditions. Despite that he was so resourceful that he was able to make great collections of wild life from the areas he visited. He lived closely with the native people and became familiar with their habits and way of life.

When returning from one visit to the Amazon, having been away for two years, he had brought onto the ship a great collection of specimens, all carefully packed for the voyage, together with his diaries which described all he had been doing and his notes on his specimens. Tragically the ship caught fire and all his specimens and notes were destroyed. Wallace accepted this dreadful setback with characteristic bravery.

Wallace came to the same conclusion as Darwin regarding Natural Selection and defended the concept strenuously, but he thought that it could not account for modern man. He clearly saw that people's minds were *better than needed* for the simple lives of the people that he had been living with, and therefore had not developed by a process of Natural Selection. Perhaps because he strongly believed in the spiritual side of life he was more able than Darwin was to accept that there were limitations to Natural Selection, and that the appearance of modern people required some further explanation.

In the spring of 1858, Wallace wrote a letter to Darwin, telling him about some ideas he had following his studies in the Malay Archipelago. When Darwin read the letter, he was surprised to see that Wallace was thinking along similar lines to himself regarding Natural Selection and evolution. Lyell and Hooker arranged that papers by both men were read to the Linnaean Society in London, on July 1st 1858. Darwin did not attend because he was grief stricken over the death of his youngest child, a son, from scarlet fever only three days before the meeting. Wallace did not attend either as he was overseas; the papers were read by the secretary of the Society. Following the stimulus from Wallace, Darwin worked very hard to complete the book that he had been labouring over for many years. This was published in November 1859 under the title *"The Origin of Species by Means of Natural Selection"* with the subtitle *"The preservation of favoured races in the struggle for life"*. (4) The book immediately aroused wide interest in the scientific circles of the day, throughout Europe. It was both strongly praised and vigorously attacked, but in the end was accepted with some reservations by most contemporary biologists. Wallace also published a book recording his own ideas, in 1870, under the title *"On Natural Selection"*. (5) Although Wallace and Darwin agreed on so much, there was a fundamental difference between them. Darwin sought to demonstrate that Natural Selection could explain the development of humans, including modern man. Wallace disagreed with this. He refused to believe that modern man could result from the unaided operation of Natural Selection. Sir Charles Lyell also had great difficulty with this, writing in *The geological evidences for the antiquity of man* "There remains profound mystery how the huge gulf between man and beast could be bridged."

With *The Origin of Species* Darwin convinced his contemporaries about evolution: that plants and animals had developed slowly over a long period of time, but many were unconvinced about the role of Natural Selection and its importance for evolution.

In brief, Natural Selection depends upon the following deductions.

1. All animals and plants produce large numbers of offspring but the size of the adult population remains broadly the same, indicating that there is great loss of life, especially in the young.
2. The members of a species of animals or plants are not all identical. They show variation in many of their characteristics.
3. Although much loss of life is due to chance events, the environment and life experiences will tend, over a period of time, to favour the variants which are best fitted to their surroundings.
4. The result is a differential survival of certain advantageous qualities.
5. If the favourable variant is due to a heritable quality it will, over time, become present in all members of the species.

It is important to avoid confusion between evolution and Natural Selection. Evolution is a process of development that has evidently been in progress for many millions of years, and there is no doubt about that. Natural Selection is a theory advanced by Darwin and Wallace, which attempts to explain how evolution works. How well it does this is open to some debate.

There had been much discussion about natural theology and science in the decades before *Origin of Species* was published. A very interesting and beautifully written introduction to this is the essay by John Hedley Brooke: *Scientific thought and its meaning for religion. The impact of French science on British natural theology, 1827–1859.* (6) He demonstrates the way in which the work of some great French scientists (Cuvier, Lamarck, Laplace and Geoffroy Saint-Hilaire) was transferred to Britain by contemporary British scientists (William Buckland, Charles Lyell, William Whewell and Richard Owen) in a way that reduced its conflict with religion, but rather aligned it with natural theology.

One can speculate about whether Darwin's work would have caused much interest in the general public had it not been grasped by some atheists, who saw it as a stick with which to beat the Church and a way to try to discredit the authority of the Bible. Chief of Darwin's scientific supporters was Thomas Henry Huxley (1825–1895). He also undertook a surveying expedition to the South Seas, on board HMS Rattlesnake, from 1846 to 1850. He became a foremost biologist. He took part in the famous debate at the British Academy meeting in Oxford, in 1860, in which he is said to have declared to Bishop Samuel Wilberforce that "he would rather be descended from an ape than a Bishop." That is a paraphrase of what he really said, which was "A man has no reason to be ashamed of having an ape for his grandfather. If there were an ancestor whom I should feel shame in recalling it would rather be a man—a man of restless and versatile intellect—who plunges into scientific questions with which he has no real acquaintance, only to obscure them by an aimless rhetoric, and distract the attention of his hearers from the real point at issue by eloquent digressions and skilled appeals to religious prejudice."

The Churchmen of the day were not equipped to debate scientific subjects: their learning was entirely in other disciplines. Huxley later turned more to theology and philosophy himself, using the term *agnostic* to describe his views. By this, he meant that nothing can be known about the existence of God, or of anything else, other than material things. However, there were scientists contemporary with Darwin who questioned Natural Selection. For example, St George Mivart wrote in 1871: "Natural Selection is incompetent to account for the incipient stages of useful structures. That it does not harmonise with the co-existence of closely similar structures of diverse origin. That there are grounds for thinking that specific differences may be developed suddenly instead of gradually..." Very wise and penetrating objections that are still expressed and are still valid today.

The problem was that Darwin said that animals and plants were not created specially and individually by God, but had developed slowly over a long period of time, by a natural process. He also said that humans had descended from earlier ancestors who had given rise to both man and the apes. These ideas were totally unacceptable to the religious leaders of the time. They found them so offensive to both God and man that they were unable to think calmly about the implications.

Most praise for advancing the understanding of evolution is given to Charles Darwin. It is interesting to speculate upon how much Darwin might have been influenced by *Vestiges*. It is clear therein that their author puts forward a "Hypothesis of Development" that on careful reading has many similarities with Natural Selection, for example in *Vestiges*, page 202:

"The tendency of all these illustrations is to make us look to *development* as the principle which has been immediately concerned in the peopling of this globe, a process extending over a vast space of time, but which is nevertheless connected in character with the briefer process by which an individual being is evoked from a simple germ. What mystery is there here—and how shall I proceed to enunciate the conception which I have ventured to form of what may prove to be its proper solution! It is an idea by no means calculated to impress by its greatness, or to puzzle by its profoundness. It is an idea more marked by simplicity than perhaps any other of those which have explained the great secrets of nature. But in this lies, perhaps, one of its strongest claims to the faith of mankind."

"The whole train of animated beings, from the simplest and oldest up to the highest and most recent, are, then, to be regarded as a series of *advances of the principle of development*, which have depended upon external physical circumstances, to which the resulting animals are appropriate. I contemplate the whole phenomena as having been in the first place arranged in the counsels of the Divine Wisdom, to take place, not only upon this sphere, but upon all the others in space, under necessary modifications, and as being carried on, from first to last, here and elsewhere, under immediate favour of the creative will or energy."

"The nucleated vesicle (by which he meant the fertilised ovum), the fundamental form of all organisation, we must regard as the meeting-point between the inorganic and the organic—the end of the mineral and beginning of the vegetable and animal kingdoms, which thence start in different directions but in perfect parallelism and analogy. We have already seen that this nucleated vesicle is itself a kind of mature and independent being in the infusory animalcules, as well as the starting point of the foetal progress of every higher individual in creation, both animal and vegetable." (Emphasis in original, underlining added).

The realisation that embryonic development was a mirror of evolutionary development was a brilliant insight by Robert Chambers. The idea was later formulated into Ernst Haeckel's Law, in the 1920s, which stated that *ontogeny recapitulates phylogeny*. (Meaning that the stages of development of the embryo recapitulate the stages of evolutionary development of animals.) The modern version is "Ontogeny *creates* phylogeny." While this is true in broad outline, it does not hold true in detail. Some embryologists at the time tried to align what was known about embryology with what was known about evolution, but it became obvious that this was not going to have any epistemic value and the concept was no longer studied.

Scientific interest in the relationship between embryology and evolution was revived later by the work of Stephen Jay Gould. In 1977, he wrote a book titled *Ontogeny and Phylogeny* in which he explained the conflicting results of previous research and introduced his own explanations for the development of embryos. Gould proposed that there were mechanisms that control the rate at which an organism grows, and others which control the rate at which it changes shape over time. Random mutations can alter the rate at which these changes take effect, speeding up or slowing down the speed at which the embryo of a species develops. These changing rates of development can have a profound effect on the entire body shape of an individual, or upon the form of a particular organ. These varying rates of change are known as *heterochrony*, which is mediated by regulatory genes.

Coming back to Robert Chambers' theory of *development*, the "external physical circumstances" which lead to the resulting animals being "appropriate" to them is a clear statement of the same principles as those that support and define Natural Selection: not stated quite as strongly as in *The Origin,* but nevertheless a clear indication of the idea, which Chambers calls "his hypothesis". Robert Chambers should be given full credit for this, but he has been largely forgotten in the movement to honour Darwin and nobody else. Robert Chambers agrees completely with the idea that God created everything, it is only the manner in which this was done that requires further consideration. Darwin's religious beliefs have been the subject of much study and some uncertainty, but there is support for the view that Darwin did believe that Natural Selection was the way in which God created the natural world. It was only his atheist supporters who thought otherwise.

Alfred Russell Wallace has not been given nearly enough credit for the theory of Natural Selection, which he exactly visualised at the same time as Darwin, and which he championed vigorously alongside Darwin. Perhaps this was because Wallace stopped short of attributing the existence of people to the action of Natural Selection alone. The theory of Natural Selection should really be referred to as the Darwin and Wallace theory, although Wallace himself seemed content to let Darwin take the credit. He wrote in the preface to his book *On Natural Selection*, "I have felt all my life, and I still feel, the most sincere satisfaction that Mr Darwin had been at work long before me, and that it was not left for me to attempt to write *The Origin of Species*. I have long since measured my own strength, and know well that it would be quite unequal to that task." Wallace was rather overshadowed by Darwin, perhaps because, although they were both gentlemen, Darwin had a higher place in Society due to his greater wealth, through his marriage in 1839 to his cousin Emma Wedgwood. Wallace was always short of money and at times had to sell some of his specimens to survive. He also had an interest in Spiritualism, which made some of the other leading scientists of the day question his judgement and objectivity.

Darwin admitted in a letter to Hooker that he got his inspiration mainly from artificial selective breeding of domestic animals. Wallace in his letters and autobiography said that his inspiration came from recollecting the writing of Robert Malthus (1766–1834) *On Population*, especially his "checks" on population growth, namely war, famine and disease. Both built on their ideas with widespread references to their observations of animals and plants, which they had both gathered during their extensive naturalist journeyings.

It is greatly to the credit of Darwin that he organised a petition to the Prime Minister (William Gladstone) to ask that Wallace be given a Government pension. Darwin put great effort into this, helped by Huxley and others, eventually persuading eleven of the greatest contemporary men of science to add their names to his. In 1881, Gladstone granted a pension of £200 a year (somewhat backdated). This enabled Wallace to live from the age of 58 in modest comfort for the rest of his life.

After a short period of controversy, Darwin's theory of Natural Selection became generally accepted by most scientists for some years, but after the work of Gregor Mendel became widely known and understood, Darwin's theory fell into disrepute. It was also pointed out by Henry Charles Fleeming Jenkin, in an article published in 1867, that Darwin's theory of Pangenesis (if true) would have resulted in an averaging out, or blending of characteristics, which would have made Natural Selection impossible. Jenkin was Regius Professor of Engineering at the University of Edinburgh, and a multi-talented man. He became famous through his invention of the cable-car. Darwin wrote in a letter to Joseph Hooker "Fleeming Jenkin has given me much trouble, but has been of more real use than any other essay or review." Darwin changed his views somewhat in response to Jenkin's criticism.

Mendel had published his work in a little-known journal (as described earlier in this chapter) and it remained largely unknown for many years. It was remarkable that towards the end of the nineteenth century two botanists began independent plant breeding experiments which were closely similar to the work of Mendel, without any knowledge of either Mendel's work or of each other.

Hugo Marie de Vries (1848–1935) was a Dutch botanist and geneticist. He worked on plant breeding experiments and independently discovered the laws of heredity in the 1890s without any knowledge of the previous work by Mendel. He introduced into genetics the terms *gene* and *mutation*.

Carl Erich Correns (1864–1933) was a German botanist and geneticist who independently discovered the principles of heredity and was also the person who later found and publicised Mendel's original paper. He was the first to demonstrate that in plants there is also cytoplasmic inheritance as well as Mendelian inheritance mediated by genes.

Most educated people know the name of Gregor Mendel as the founder of the science of genetics, but few have heard of de Vries or Correns. Of course, Mendel was the first, but de Vries and Correns deserve to be remembered and honoured for their brilliant work in this field that was done before either had read Mendel's paper. One of the minor purposes of this book is to try to see that credit is given where it is due, which does not always happen in science or life in general.

Following this it was accepted that Mendelian inheritance was correct: it was scientifically sound and reliable. In fact, not very long after that Mendel's Law of Independent Assortment had to be modified because of the discovery of *linkage*. This is the tendency of DNA sequences that are close together on a chromosome to be inherited together during meiosis. The concept of the gene then changed from being a single entity to being something much more complex. It consists of one or more *introns*, which are the largest elements in a gene and encode for a particular polypeptide during protein synthesis. Within the intron, there are one or more *exons*. These are locations within the gene which participate in recombination. Each exon may have within it one or more *mutons*. These are elements within a gene that can undergo a mutation. Many mutons within an exon may stay linked because of recombination.

It was then thought that Mendelian inheritance was not compatible with the principles of Natural Selection and it was completely different from Darwin's own theories of genetics. As a consequence of these two deficiencies Darwin was discredited for many years. Some alternative theories were proposed at that time, but have not survived. One theory that was well supported before the *Origin* was published was known as Saltationism. (The name derives from a Latin verb *salire* meaning a leap or jump.) This proposes that evolution progresses through large step-like changes. Darwin firmly believed that Natural Selection worked by large numbers of small changes over a long period of time—gradualism—which was contrary to Saltationism. The idea of large changes was revived by the work of Richard Benedict Goldschmidt (1878–1958), a German-born American geneticist. He is considered to be the first person to attempt to integrate genetics, development and evolution. He suggested that macroevolution must depend on macro-mutations which would cause very marked phenotypic change in an individual, producing what came to be known as "hopeful monsters". He thought that these could rapidly produce new species. This has been more or less dismissed now, but he did perceptively suggest that there must be "rate genes" or "controlling genes" which change early embryonic development and therefore cause large effects in the adult phenotype. This has been shown to be true in recent decades. Present day advocates of Saltationism claim that new body plans come into being as a result of sudden discontinuous changes, leading to the appearance of new higher taxa, including Classes and Orders, while small variation is thought to be responsible for the fine adaptations below species level.

There was then a reappraisal of Darwin's theory by leading scientists in the early years of the twentieth Century, stimulated by work on population genetics and statistics. There was a lot of controversy between supporters of various conflicting ideas. This was eventually resolved by the painstaking work of Sir Julian Huxley (1887–1975), who was a grandson of T.H. Huxley. Sir Julian was Secretary of the Zoological Society of London and a leading evolutionary biologist and philosopher himself. He was personally known to many of the various proponents. He consulted widely, and published *Evolution: The Modern Synthesis* in 1942. Huxley's main co-respondents in writing the book are listed as Ernst Mayr, Theodosius Dobzhansky, Gaylord Simpson, Bernhard Rensch, Ledyard Stebbins and the population geneticists J.B.S. Haldane, Ronald Fisher and Sewall Wright.

Theodosius Dobzhansky was a Soviet-born geneticist who emigrated from Russia to the United States in 1928 where he worked on genetics using populations of flies. He was strongly influenced by the findings of the population geneticist Sewall Wright, who showed that the size of a population can affect the rate at which mutations can spread. At that time, it was thought that all members of a species had almost identical genes, based largely on laboratory studies. Dobzhansky travelled to Mexico to catch wild fruit flies of the species *Drosophila pseudoobscura*. He found that different populations of these flies did not have identical genes; they carried distinctive markers in their chromosomes which distinguished them from other populations of the same species. This raised the question "What defines a species if its genes are not all the same?" Dobzhansky realised that the species, in either animals or plants, was defined by sex. A species is a group of animals or plants that breed only among themselves. They are unable to breed outside the species to produce hybrids that can themselves produce viable offspring. He showed from experiments with fruit flies that this was caused by specific genes carried by one species that interfere with the genes from a separate species. However today there are several competing species concepts which are still hotly debated.

Dobzhansky published *Genetics and the Origin of Species* in 1937. In the book, he described how he envisaged the way in which new species came into existence. The starting point is the continuous occurrence of mutations, some of

103

which are harmful, but most of which are harmless. These neutral mutations appear in different populations and persist, leading to much more variability than had been supposed previously. [But only mutations in germ-line cells are heritable.] This variability is the basis for making new species but also depends on a group of flies being isolated from others of the same species, so that the isolated group breeds only within the group. New mutations would arise in the isolated group and after a time they might be present in all the flies, possibly aided by Natural Selection if the mutation was advantageous. Over time this isolated group would become more and more genetically different from the rest of the species. Some of the new genes might be incompatible with some genes in the other members of the species that were separated from the group. After a time, these flies might be unable to breed with the others from outside the group, even if their isolation broke down for some reason. They would be unable to mate, or would produce offspring which were themselves infertile. In this way, a new species would have been produced.

Dobzhansky's *Genetics and the Origin of Species* seen together with Darwin's *Origin of Species* aroused great interest amongst many scientists of diverse disciplines. One of these was an ornithologist called Ernst Mayr who was studying the wild bird life in the mountains of New Guinea. He specialised in identifying new species of birds and defining the location and area of their habitat. He studied Birds of Paradise, and found that it was often difficult to decide which were in separate species. He found that birds from different areas, with similar coloured plumage, might differ from each other in some other important characteristics. For example, he found that the tails of Birds of Paradise living in the mountains of western New Guinea were longer than those of birds living in the central mountains, which were more squared off.

Mayr published a book in 1942, called *Systematics and the Origin of Species,* which presented results from his many observations. He argued that the most significant way to separate a population of organisms was by geographical isolation. He gave the example of a glacier forcing its way down a valley to produce two separate habitats on either side of the glacier, with two separate populations of animals and plants, one on either side. Another example was the way in which a rising sea-level could turn a peninsula into a chain of islands, such as the Isthmus of Panama, isolating the animals to their particular island. Isolation like this need only last long enough for the separated populations to develop distinctive genotypes so that they become incompatible with each other.

After that, the separated groups of animals will be unable to interbreed and will remain separate species. Geographical isolation is still thought to be a very important cause of speciation, but more recently it is also thought that it may be possible for a population to continue breeding with other members of its species while still diverging into a distinctive group or that animals and plants can diverge into genetically distinctive populations even though they are living close to one another. This is referred to as "Ecological speciation" or "Sympatric speciation". For example, this could be due to different mating preferences amongst the females, which could strengthen over time to form a kind of reproductive isolation. Mayr's examples of the glacier and the peninsula given above would not happen very often.

Population genetics arose mainly through the work of Ronald Fisher (1890–1962), a research biologist at the Rothamstead Experimental Station in East Anglia, UK, in the 1920s. He developed statistical methods which have been of immense value in many fields of science. He has been described as "a genius who almost single-handedly created the foundations for modern statistical science." Fisher used his mathematical brilliance to show that Mendelian genetics was not incompatible with Darwinian Natural Selection, which helped to restore Darwin's reputation. The details of Fisher's work are only understandable by other statisticians and mathematicians and lie outside the scope of this book.

When Huxley's book was published, it was widely acclaimed as a work of great scholarship. In the first chapter Huxley wrote in some detail about the way in which Darwin fell into disrepute and the reasons for this. The original concept of Natural Selection still had merit but the underlying mechanisms envisaged by Darwin were not correct. This was well expressed at the time by a distinguished biologist called Lancelot Hogben (1895–1975), who had carried out valuable work using the Xenopus frog to demonstrate that changes in skin colour were due to the action of the pituitary gland. He also showed that female Xenopus frogs ovulated soon after injection with pituitary extract and his assistants later developed this information into a pregnancy test by injecting a woman's urine into the frogs. If the woman was pregnant, it contained human chorionic gonadotrophin, which would rapidly cause ovulation in the frog. Hogben was also one of the first to see the importance and interdependence of both "nature" and "nurture" as separate entities, that is to say, the separation of the effects of inheritance from the effects of upbringing, and throughout his life championed the cause of maintaining the importance of nurture, being unwilling to give over-riding importance to the gene.

Hogben wrote thus: "Darwin interpreted the process of artificial selection in terms of a theory of *blending inheritance*, universally accepted by his own generation, whereas the modern view is based on the theory of Particulate Inheritance. The consequences of these two views are very different." Darwin saw evolution as a continuous process but the later biologists saw it as discontinuous.

Blending inheritance was shown to be untrue. Darwin's Pangenesis was shown to be untrue. Darwin's support for Lamarck and the inheritance of acquired characteristics was shown to be misplaced. All that was left was the role of Selection acting on Variation. [However, recent work—after the year 2000—has shown that epigenetic effects do provide, to some extent, a mechanism for inheritance of acquired characteristics, not involving the genome. This is discussed later.] Hogben and others thought that the use of the names Darwinism and Natural Selection should be discontinued. They thought that the importance of Selection was much less than Darwin had supposed and that Darwin's contribution was not enough to justify continued use of those names. Huxley defended the use of the names, and hence Darwin himself. He pointed out that in Physics the name "atom" had been retained, even though it originally indicated an indivisible particle but was now known to be made up of sub-particles, which was a precedent for retaining Darwinism and Natural Selection. He said that "…biologists may with a good heart continue to be Darwinians and to employ the term Natural Selection, even if Darwin knew nothing of mendelising mutations, and if selection is by itself incapable of changing the constitution of a species or a line." It was this kindly and generous support by Julian Huxley, in the tradition of his grandfather, which salvaged Darwin's reputation. He wrote further "The Darwinism thus reborn is a modified Darwinism, since it must operate with facts unknown to Darwin, but it is still Darwinism in the sense that it aims at giving a naturalistic interpretation of evolution."

Over the decades since that time the deficiencies in Darwin's ideas about evolution seem to have been largely forgotten, and he has been greatly honoured. He deserves to be honoured for his painstaking work, his great powers of observation, his prolific writing and his humanity, but the contribution that he made on Natural Selection should be seen in balance. It was a profound idea of great importance but it had been previously published by Chambers and simultaneously proposed by Wallace. Understanding how Natural Selection contributes to evolution depends on advances in knowledge of biology at the molecular level, which were completely unknown to Darwin. It is only a part of the story and it will be a continuing study for years to come.

Julian Huxley's book *Evolution: the Modern Synthesis*, first published in 1942 and subsequently re-printed, is quite a large book. It became the foundation for the modern understanding of evolution and has remained more or less in this position until recent years, but there have been further important developments since that time, as described below. The book included all that was known at that time about evolution and genetics. It is written in an exceptionally clear and pleasing style. It remains a landmark publication and a fount of information.

Huxley placed great emphasis on the importance of selection acting on variation, mediated by Mendelian inheritance. He wrote "We should begin as Darwin did, with the fact of variation, and deduce from it and our previous deduction of the struggle for existence that there must be a *differential survival* of different types of offspring in each generation. [Meaning that there are different survival rates in different individuals]…Natural Selection is thus seen to have two rather different meanings. In a broad sense, it covers all cases of differential survival; but from the evolutionary point of view it covers only the differential transmission of inheritable variation."

He explained at length and with many examples the reasons why Lamarckian inheritance was incorrect. This was necessary at that time because there was still a lot of interest in the concept of the inheritance of acquired characteristics and Huxley found it necessary to refute the writings of a number of respected biologists who still supported Lamarck's theory. Several chapters were devoted to various aspects of speciation. Huxley supported Mayr's ideas about geographic isolation and the idea of reproductive isolation. He also emphasised the importance of adaptation in evolution which is always present. He gave many examples of how adaptation was manifested. Huxley recognised that the extent of variation seen in different species was widely dissimilar, giving the example of the contrast between the uniformity of snipe and most ducks as against the tendency of many species of passerine birds to break up into geographical sub-species. He said "Much work must be done before we can do more than guess" about what causes the restriction of actual variability. He ends the book with a consideration of evolutionary progress: "Is this a scientific concept?" He defined what he meant by evolutionary progress, and described its nature and mechanism, going on to describe past progress and to speculate about evolutionary progress in the future. He updated the book in 1963 and 1974. Huxley wrote a perceptive introduction to the 1963 edition, which included information about the newly discovered structure of DNA. The introduction to the 1974 edition was written by a panel of nine experts who represented the many disciplines involved in the huge increase in knowledge since the previous edition. Neither of the new editions introduced any significant changes to the foundational concepts of the *Synthesis*.

In 1972, a paper was written by Niels Eldredge and Stephen Jay Gould (7) which is generally accepted as the origin of the concept of Punctuated Equilibrium. (Distinct from Saltation.) This theory, which applies to any sexually reproducing species, posits that in most cases there will be little net evolutionary change over most of the species' geological existence. For most of the time, it will remain essentially unchanged in a state known as "stasis". The stasis is interrupted by sudden rare but rapidly occurring bursts of change, which lead to the species suddenly branching into two new species. This is known as cladogenesis. But it must be remembered that sudden change is relative to geological time, so that what a palaeontologist calls sudden might be 50,000 years out of a species lifetime of five million years.

It is not known why there are these rapidly occurring bursts of change: why do they occur when they do and what is the mechanism? Punctuated equilibrium depends heavily on isolation of members of a species from the rest of the species. Once a species has become established there is little change between generations because the changes do not accumulate: the species varies around its phenotypic mean.

When the Eldredge and Gould paper was published, it caused quite a lot of controversy and it seemed an important departure from Darwin's concept. But more recently this difference has been played down, notably by the geneticist Richard Dawkins. In his book "*The Blind Watchmaker*" (8) he suggests that there are probably a lot of different rates of change involved in evolution, depending on circumstances: they all fit into a neo-Darwinian theory. Darwin himself recognised that species did not all change at the same rate and that "the periods during which species have undergone modification, though long in years, have probably been short in comparison with the periods during which they retain the same form." Darwin eventually thought that isolation of a group within a species was of relatively little importance compared with the effect of the size of the area in which the species lived. The area available for life determined the size of the population and the amount of change the species would experience, together with the extent and diversity of challenges in the environment and from other developing species. The larger the area the greater the variation and change.

Recent years have seen the emergence of the theory of Intelligent Design, which has been touched upon in other chapters. This is a scientific theory about the development of biochemical pathways, which has crucial importance for evolution. But intelligent design has generated a surprising amount of hostility from both some scientists and some church people. This is probably because it is misunderstood, often being over simplified to nothing more than a marvelling at the complexity of living organisms. It is much more than that, and needs to be thought about at the molecular level. Probably the best exposition of intelligent design is the book by the professor of biochemistry, Michael Behe, *"Darwin's black box"* (9). This is a remarkable book which was an inspiration to me when it was first published in 1996. It should be emphasised that this is not in any way a religious book: on the contrary it is a highly scientific book which focuses on the biochemical pathways which are fundamental to life. *Darwin's Black Box* is a milestone in biology, because it marks the transition from the anatomical to the biochemical. No longer can one describe things only in terms of what they look like macroscopically. There has to be a biochemical explanation of how they work at the molecular level.

The black box is the living cell, the contents of which were mainly unknown to Darwin but are now understood in amazing detail. The theory depends on the concept that there are irreducibly complex systems. Behe gives the example of a mouse trap. It is made of five simple components. All these components have to be of the correct manufacture and assembled in the right way for the mouse trap to work. If any one component is not exactly as it should be, the mouse trap will not operate. He then goes on to consider much more complicated irreducibly complex systems, such as the cilia on a cell surface and the biochemical pathways in the light sensitive cells of the retina. Behe says: "An irreducibly complex system cannot be produced directly (that is, by continuously improving the initial function, which continues to work by the same mechanism) by slight, successive modifications of a precursor system, because any precursor to an irreducibly complex system that is missing one part is by definition non-functional." He rightly points out that much of what is written about evolution concerns gross anatomy, but that understanding the structure of organs depends on understanding their constituent cells and especially the biochemical pathways that enable them to function. Studies of evolution have tended to focus on the macro scale and rather gloss over the great difficulties of understanding events at the molecular level, until recently. Intelligent design as described by Behe is compelling. It is a scientific question which must be studied at the molecular level. It is outside the scope of this book to consider it in any detail, but it deserves much more respect than it gets from scientists and theologians. It does not provide answers: rather it poses questions that are difficult to answer.

So what people should say about intelligent design is that there are some processes that are not susceptible to explanation by the concepts of Natural Selection. This must be true by definition. A complex biochemical pathway, such as the photo-activation of a retinal cell, could not have arisen from the unaided operation of Natural Selection, because the early or intermediate stages, indeed anything short of the full cascade of reactions, will confer no advantage on which selection can operate (as argued by St George Mivert in 1871). So what intelligent design does is to point to either the existence of a designer or the existence of some form of evolution that is not dependent on the selection of advantageous features. Some might say that it would be sufficient if the intermediate steps of a complex process were established by mutations that do not confer *disadvantage*. Then, when the critical final mutation occurs and the whole complex system or cascade clicks into action a sudden and great advantage may be conferred. The counter-argument is that there are very large numbers of irreducibly complex pathways and for these to arise by the chance accumulation of potentially useful and harmless mutations would be statistically very rare events that might account for a few but not the majority of such systems.

To take one example, the biochemical pathway that reacts to a photon of light by producing a nerve impulse is extremely complicated, as is the pathway that returns the system to the starting point, ready for the next stimulus. It would take two pages of text to give even an abridged summary of the processes involved. In brief, the starting point is the photon reacting with 11-*cis*-retinol in a few picoseconds to produce trans-retinal. All-trans-retinal is a molecule with the formula $C_{20} H_{28} O$. The chemical name for this is:

3,7-dimethyl-9-(2,6,6-trimethyl-1-cyclohexen-1-yl)-2,4,6,8-tetraenal.

After photo-activation the trans-retinal then changes shape to become rhodopsin, which attaches to transducin and a small molecule called GTP. The GTP-transducin-metarhodopsin then binds to phosphodiesterase, which can then cut cGMP. When cGMP levels in the cell fall there is a fall in sodium ions: Na^+. This causes an imbalance of positive charge across the cell membrane, which generates an electrical impulse. That travels along the optic nerve to the brain to contribute to the building of a visual image. By another complex series of molecular changes, the system rapidly reverts to the starting state.

What is perhaps most amazing about all of this is the speed at which these biochemical reactions work. When one looks ahead, then looks to the side, the whole visual image has to be reconstructed. Imagine the amount of biochemistry needed to do that throughout the eye, in a fraction of a second so small that it appears to be instantaneous.

Despite the attempt to side-line intelligent design outside science, some work has been done to address the problems it represents. One such is the idea that there could be some kind of matrix on which biochemical systems are built, rather like the scaffolding that supports a building during its construction. However, it is difficult to envisage how such a structure would itself evolve. We await a detailed, credible description of how irreducibly complex pathways can occur without design.

It is almost impossible to imagine what is going on at the molecular level within cells. The very large molecules of DNA, RNA, proteins, enzymes and substrates lie in close proximity to one another, in an aqueous milieu, yet they manage to carry out specific syntheses without interfering with each other. Continuing research has led to these biochemical pathways becoming more completely understood, for example in genomics.

By the 1980s, biologists began to identify genes that were involved in development of the embryo. Nowadays there is much known about the way in which some genes send signals to other genes, which then induce embryonic cells to multiply or die, or to stick together or to move to some other place. Gould correctly predicted that these types of control mechanisms would not be mediated by genes that induced the making of body parts but by distinct regulatory genes. Many of these regulatory genes go a long way back in evolutionary history.

In the last decade, much work has been done on molecular evolution, which studies the way in which genes have developed at the molecular level. So called

Evo-Devo shows that foetal development is closely controlled by genetic systems. The Nobel Prize winner Edward B. Lewis (10) showed that there are genes which activate or repress certain cellular processes which determine the final development of the organism. Thus one cluster of master control genes programmes the development of all higher organisms.

The Modern Synthesis remained the orthodox view of evolution for most biologists up until the end of the twentieth century, but in the first decade of the new millennium there began to be increasing calls for a re-evaluation of the Modern Synthesis in the light of the many new ideas that were emerging, in various biological disciplines, in relation to evolution. In response to this a meeting was held at the Konrad Lorenz Institute for Evolution and Cognition Research in Altenberg, Austria, in July 2008. A group of sixteen prominent evolutionary biologists and philosophers of science met, over three days, to discuss the new information from a number of different fields, and some conceptual changes were seen to emerge, both from traditional subjects such as quantitative genomics and from new fields of research such as Evo-Devo. This led to the publication of a book in 2010 based on the conclusions of the meeting, edited by Massimo Pigliucci and Gerd B. Muller, which they called *Evolution: the Extended Synthesis* (11) with seventeen chapters contributed by twenty experts from several disciplines.

The book begins with a discussion about whether the term Extended Synthesis can be justified. Some experts in the field dispute this, but there is no doubt that present day biology goes far beyond what was known when the Modern Synthesis was last updated in 1974, so it does seem both reasonable and useful to establish a demarcation at this time, even though the contents of the Extended Synthesis may not be widely agreed yet and may remain contentious for some time to come.

In the introductory chapter of the book, Pigliucci and Muller explain that the Extended Synthesis overcomes several basic restrictions and methodological commitments that had been necessary for the correlational approach of the Modern Synthesis to work: Gradualism, Externalism and Gene centrism. They wrote:

Gradualism

"Because the population-dynamic formalism operated on the assumption of continuous and incremental genetic variation, all non-gradualist forms of evolutionary change were excluded. Several approaches discussed in this volume show that non-gradual change is a property of complex dynamical systems, including biological organisms, and that various kinds of mechanisms for discontinuous change are now known from the domains of genome evolution, phenotypic plasticity, epigenetic development and non-genetic inheritance. The dynamics of biological systems illuminates the capacity of continuous selective regimes to produce the non-gradual phenotypic change frequently observed in the paleontological record. Accounting for these forms of discontinuous change amounts to a significant extension of the evolutionary synthesis."

Comment. The idea that evolution took place in large steps was current at the end of the nineteenth century, when it was called Saltationism, but this was excluded by Darwinism, especially in the Modern Synthesis. The concept was revived in a slightly different form by Etheredge and Gould in 1972, who called it *punctuated equilibrium.* However the lack of intermediate forms in the fossil record could be due to the relatively small number of intermediates compared with the large number of specimens from the settled form of the organism. The extended synthesis gives much more weight to sudden large changes to an organism compared with a long series of continuous small changes. The major question is: Do genome evolution, phenotypic plasticity, epigenetic development and non-genetic inheritance have a large enough effect to be significant in evolution? In other words, do they have a major impact or only a marginal effect?

Externalism

"The nearly exclusive concentration of the Modern Synthesis on Natural Selection gave priority to all external factors that realise adaptation through differential reproduction, a fundamental feature of Darwinism. Organismal shape and structure were interpreted as products uniquely of external selection regimes. All directionality of the evolutionary process was assumed to result from Natural Selection alone. Evo-Devo represents a major change of this paradigm by taking the contributions of the generative processes into account, as entrenched properties of the organism promote particular forms of change rather than others. On this view, Natural Selection becomes a constantly operating background condition, but the specificity of its phenotypic outcome is provided by the developmental systems it operates on. Hence the organisms themselves represent the determinants of selectable variation and innovation. At the theoretical level this shifts a significant portion of the explanatory weight from the external conditions of selection to the internal generative properties of evolving phenotypes."

Comment. Evo-Devo states that properties of the organism affect the development of the embryo and therefore the nature of the phenotypic variants that are produced. But it is still the environment that selects the most fitted individuals. How much effect does Evo-Devo have in practical terms? The balance between external influences (Natural Selection) and internal influences (Evo-Devo) is not known at present.

Gene centrism

"The focus on the gene as the sole agent of variation and unit of inheritance, and the dogmatic insistence on this stance by the popularisers of the Synthesis, quelled all calls for more comprehensive attitudes. Although gene centrism [Meaning that only the gene can affect inheritance] has been a major source of contention…it could not be changed from within the paradigm of the Modern Synthesis, which rested on it both explicitly and implicitly. But gene centrism necessarily disappears in an extended account that provides for multi-causal evolutionary factors acting on organismal systems' properties, including the non-programmed components of the environment, development and inheritance. Far from denying the importance of genes in organismal evolution, the extended theory gives less overall weight to genetic variation as a generative force. Rather, the opinions expressed in several contributions to this volume converge on the view of 'genes as followers' in the evolutionary process, ensuring the routinisation of developmental interactions, the faithfulness of their inheritance, and the progressive fixation of phenotypic traits that were initially mobilised through plastic responses of adaptive developmental systems to changing environmental conditions. In this way, evolution progresses through the capture of emergent interactions into genetic—epigenetic circuits, which are passed to and elaborated on in subsequent generations."

Comment. "Plastic responses of adaptive developmental systems to changing environmental conditions" sounds like Natural Selection. What is the mechanism, frequency and extent of the "progressive fixation of phenotypic traits that were initially mobilised through plastic responses?"

The seventeen chapters of the book are grouped under the headings: Introduction, Variation & selection, Evolving genomes, Inheritance & replication, Evolutionary developmental biology, Macro-evolution &

evolvability and Philosophical dimensions. The main foundations on which the Extended Synthesis rests are (1) The occurrence of non-gradual, that is sudden and large changes in an organism; (2) The reduced importance of Natural Selection, especially relative to Variation, and the effects of Evolutionary Development, which further undermine the importance of Natural Selection because the organism itself has an effect on the outcome of selective events; (3) The proposal that the gene can no longer be seen as the sole instrument of selection and inheritance. There are other influences on inheritance that are not mediated through genes and DNA. One gene may give rise to several phenotypes and this phenotypic plasticity can be inherited through the action of various epigenetic processes. According to this view genes can play a secondary role of fixing the phenotypic changes and ensuring their faithful reproduction in later generations. The role of prions in inheritance further reduces the exclusivity of the genome.

The book provides an authoritative account of the state of knowledge of the subjects covered at that time. A case is made to justify the use of the term Extended Synthesis, but it is unclear how much practical difference the "extended" features of the synthesis would have made to the outcome of evolution if it had been dependent only on the accepted features of the Modern Synthesis.

Since *Evolution: the Extended Synthesis* was published in 2010 there has been very much more work done on all these subjects. A striking advance is the realisation that prions are not just unusual agents responsible for some rare diseases such as Creutzfeldt-Jakob disease, Kuru, Scrapie and Bovine Spongiform Encephalitis (Mad cow disease) but are found in many animals and in plants such as yeasts. Recently they are thought to be an important mediator of inheritance. The name Prion derives from "proteinaceous infectious particle". Prions are placed in the Kingdom Archaea (formerly Prokaryotes). They are an abnormal form of a normally harmless protein. Prions multiply by inducing benign proteins to refold into the abnormal shape. The normal protein structure consists of a number of flexible coils called alpha helices. In the prion protein some of these helices are stretched into flat structures called beta-strands. The normal protein can be easily degraded by the action of protease enzymes but prion protein is more resistant and builds up over time. Prions are resistant to ultra-violet radiation which can destroy DNA and RNA, which they appear to lack. They are self-replicating. They can cause hereditary, infectious or sporadic forms of diseases such as Creutzfeldt-Jakob disease. They can arise from an inherited mutation and are therefore thought to play a part in epigenetic inheritance. Molecular mechanisms resulting in protein misfolding that are similar to those that cause the prion diseases may be involved in other neurodegenerative diseases such as Alzheimer's disease and Parkinson's disease.

Another interesting idea is the Neutral Theory of evolution, although this was first suggested 50 years ago. The Neutral Theory of molecular evolution says that at the molecular level most evolutionary changes and most of the variation within and between species is caused by genetic drift of mutant alleles, not by Natural Selection. The theory was proposed by the Japanese biologist Motoo Kimura in 1968 and independently the following year by two American biologists, Jack Lester King and Thomas Hugh Jakes. It was later amplified and described in detail by Kimura in 1983. It is suggested that the great majority of molecular differences in genomes do not have any effect on the fitness of the organism because the majority of the genome is non-coding DNA. Those molecular differences are therefore not selected for, or against, but are selectively neutral and therefore not subject to Natural Selection. However, phenotypic evolution is controlled by Natural Selection, as Darwin had supposed.

What happens to neutral mutations is decided by the sampling which takes place during reproduction, leading to genetic drift. An organism inherits a sample of the alleles from each of its parents. Which ones it has is a matter of chance. Chance also plays a large part in the survival of the organism to reproductive age. This results in a situation where the prevalence of an allele may not remain constant. It may increase or decrease, or sometimes die out altogether. Mathematical equations describing genetic drift based on accidents of sampling can be applied. So called "purifying selection" removes deleterious mutations and is very widespread, whereas "positive selection" as proposed by Darwin is rare. This has been shown to be true by the eminent population geneticist Masatoshi Nei, who maintains that evolution is driven by mutations causing any type of change to DNA, including nucleotide changes, chromosomal changes and genome duplication. All that Natural Selection can do is eliminate the less fitted genotypes. Genetic drift is greater in small populations because of the greater opportunity to choose different alleles in the next generation.

Darwin published his theory of Natural Selection which he regarded as a theory of evolution. The Modern Synthesis is not a theory of evolution but a group of observations and theories which together attempt to explain the process of evolution. Neo-Darwinism is another term that covers much the same ground. The Extended Synthesis takes this a step further with additional information and theoretical considerations. The main accepted facts that it adds are concerned with evolutionary development, genomics and epigenetics.

The Extended Synthesis is still by no means a complete and agreed account of the processes involved in evolution. There is now talk of a Post-Modern Synthesis, which takes this process a step further down the road. This is simply a recognition of the fact that evolution is based on many and diverse processes, most of which are still incompletely understood. The Modern Synthesis and the Extended Synthesis are no more than sets of propositions of varying reliability, persuasively put together under umbrella titles: they are far from being definitive statements.

It is difficult to evaluate the recent research on subjects such as epigenetics. A useful paper was published in 2015 by Ueli Grossniklaus et al (12). In the Introduction Grossniklaus wrote "Much attention has been given to the idea of transgenerational epigenetic inheritance, but fundamental questions remain regarding how much takes place and the impact this may have on organisms. Five leading experts were asked to give their views. Their responses highlight the mixture of excitement and caution that surrounds transgenerational epigenetic inheritance and the wide gulf between species in terms of our knowledge of the mechanisms that may be involved." Review articles of this kind are useful for trying to keep up to date with the rapid developments in biology that are now happening. As time goes by, more and more weight is being given to epigenetics.

There is an interesting parallelism here between evolution and particle physics. In both cases, there is an increasing involvement with smaller and smaller units (sub-units of genes and sub-units of atoms). Both subjects are becoming more and more complex and difficult to understand. It is getting harder for generalists to understand the recent advances or for a specialist to keep fully informed about all developments in their field of study. Much work remains to be done in both subjects and it will be a very long time, if ever, before there will be closure. The important thing for believers in God to keep firmly in mind is that all these ideas about evolution are scientific ideas about the nature of the physical world, dependent on the activities of atoms and their sub-units: they do not in any way affect belief in God. It is all very interesting to anyone who likes to know how things work, but has no effect on knowledge of God. Whatever is deduced about the way in which evolution works, it is only giving us some insight into what happened under God's will. There is no purely scientific explanation for the existence of people: our soul, our language, our intellect and our immortality. Only God could have given us these.

Natural Selection is an easily understandable framework for the comprehension of evolution, but it has now been augmented by many additional mechanisms of inheritance which are still under study. What is needed now is a Unified Hypothesis of evolution which includes all the elements of evolutionary theory that are currently agreed and widely accepted. It may be some time before a group of experts can convene a meeting to attempt this task.

This chapter has been mainly a historical review of the way in which ideas about evolution have emerged and developed over the past two hundred and fifty years. Some more technical aspects about Natural Selection and Variation and the newer disciplines embraced by the Extended Synthesis are discussed in the chapter: *Natural Selection and Variation.*

References

1. Chambers, R. (1844) *Vestiges of the Natural History of Creation*, London: John Churchill.
2. Stott, R. (2012) *Darwin's Ghosts*, London: Bloomsbury Publishing.
3. Lyell, C. (1873) *Geological evidences for the antiquity of man*, London: John Murray.
4. Darwin, C (1859) *The origin of species by means of natural selection*, London: John Murray.
5. Wallace, A. R. (1871) *Contributions to the theory of Natural Selection*, London: Macmillan and Co.
6. Brooke, J. H. (1989) 'Scientific thought and its meaning for religion: the impact of French science on British natural theology', *Revue de synthese*, 4, 1, 33–59.
7. Eldredge, N. and Gould, S. J. (1972) 'Punctuated equilibrium: an alternative to phyletic gradualism', Schopf, J. M. (ed.) *Models in Paleobiology*, San Francisco: Freeman Cooper, 82–115.
8. Dawkins, R. (1986) *The blind watchmaker*, New York: Norton.
9. Behe, M. J. (1998) *Darwin's black box*, New York: Touchstone.

10. Lewis, E. B. (1995) 'The *bithorax* complex: the first fifty years. Nobel Prize lecture', Repr. In Ringertz. N. (ed.) (1997) *Nobel lectures, Physiology or Medicine.* Singapore: World Scientific.

11. Pigliucci, M. and Muller, G. B. (eds.) (2010) *Evolution: The Extended Synthesis,* Cambridge Massachusetts, MIT Press.

12. Grossniklaus, U., Willian, G., Kelly, A. C., Ferguson-Smith, M. P. and Lindquist, S. (2013) *Nat Rev Genet,* 14, 3, 228–35.

3. Natural Selection, Variation and Epigenetics

Darwin proposed the theory of Natural Selection without knowing about genetics. By the time of the Modern Synthesis, there was a lot known about genetics, although this was still mainly at the functional level rather than the molecular level. The Modern Synthesis strongly supported the concept of Natural Selection based on random mutations as the way in which better adapted variants became more numerous, leading to evolutionary change. At that time, evolution was thought to depend entirely and exclusively on variation within a species caused by mutations in germ-line cells, which sometimes produced phenotypic changes in the organism that were susceptible to selection by external environmental influences. That has remained the predominant view, except that further research has led to the Extended Modern Synthesis which is based on advances in genomics and related subjects, at the molecular level. This takes note of non-gradual development and gives less importance to Natural Selection relative to variation. It holds that the organism itself can affect the outcome of selective events.

Natural Selection

So what is the theory that is elaborated in Charles Darwin's book *The Origin of Species*, and which is summarised by the concept of Natural Selection, sometimes referred to as survival of the fittest?

First we should clarify some definitions of words. When Darwin wrote Origin he did not mean the origin of life. His theory has nothing to do with the origin of life. What he meant was that a species originates from modification of a previous species. And *fittest* does not mean fit in the sense of someone coming out of a gym, but fittest in the sense of a jigsaw puzzle piece fitting into the surrounding pieces.

The theory is critically dependent on two activities:

1. There must be variation amongst the members of a species. They are not all identical. The individuals in each generation that is produced differ a little, in some respects, from those of the previous generation and they differ from each other. These differences are heritable, that is, they are passed on to the next generation.
2. There must be a changing environment in which the organism is living. The environment has to change in its nature, to provide new challenges and opportunities for the organisms living within.

The outcome of these two activities is that in any population of individuals of a species, there will be some that are better fitted (adapted) to their environment than others. This leads to the better fitted individuals being more likely to survive to breeding age, so therefore their genes are more likely to appear and persist in later generations than those of the less well fitted individuals. In this way, new characteristics can be perpetuated. The less well fitted individuals are eliminated by the environment, in just the same way that a designer would test a design and reject those that performed badly. The end result gives the same appearance. So Natural Selection is based on need. If a new characteristic arises that is needed; useful to the life of the individual in its current environment, it is selected for. But it is not selected for if it is not needed. An important principle underlying Darwin's Natural Selection is that the outcome is decided by the environment, and that variation is random, not directed. When a new genotype appears by mutation or recombination, there is no tendency for it to be in the direction of improved adaptation. In practice, it appears that Natural Selection seems to be more effective in eliminating the unfitted than in promoting the better fitted.

That all seems very reasonable and unremarkable, but there are some difficulties. One obvious problem about Natural Selection is that chance can play a big part in survival. It is not always the best fitted that survive. For example, if a large predatory fish swims through a shoal of hundreds of young fish, it will eat all those that are in front of its jaws, regardless of any special qualities that they might develop later. The lion takes the deer that happens to be on the periphery of the herd at the moment of attack. Slaughter of the fittest by random events must greatly slow down the selection of the new, better fitted variants.

Chance events can lead to what is called *genetic drift*: a change in frequency of an allele brought about by chance events. This is not an adaptation. Natural Selection is an adaptation of an organism to its surroundings.

Natural Selection works by selecting more fitted phenotypes, and this does not necessarily equate to the genotype. It will only affect evolution if it selects phenotypic traits that will be inherited by the progeny, that is, traits that are genetically (or epigenetically?) based.

With respect to human evolution, it is reasonable to suppose that Natural Selection led, slowly, to the eventual appearance of *Homo sapiens*. Some say that humans are more advanced than other animals, but the human body is much the same as other higher animals. It is our intellect and language that are more advanced. Natural Selection cannot explain the sudden and recent appearance of People. It cannot explain the extraordinary language and intellect that set people aside from all other life, because people have abilities far beyond what are required for the simple lives of hunter-gatherers. It was not a response to need. Natural Selection operates by physical selection of physical qualities. It cannot have any direct effect on the soul or spiritual world. What has happened is that humans evolved over millions of years but it is only recently that the human became a person. *Humans evolved but people were made.* This was done by an upgrade of the human by giving a soul, language, intellect and immortality.

Variation

Variation is fundamental to Natural Selection. Without variation, Natural Selection has nothing to work on, nothing to select for. Variation is brought about by the action of modifications to the genetic code. But it should be remarked that the primary purpose of the genetic code is to keep things the same, not to introduce change. All people alive today are the progeny of about four females, if recent studies of mitochondrial DNA are to be believed, and the differences between the genomes of different people alive today are very small. We are all essentially the same and have hardly changed genetically over the past 70 thousand years. At the same time, we do all show very many small genetic variations from one another, in many characteristics, and it must be remembered that a small change in the genetic code can sometimes produce a large change in the phenotype. Many genes control only a single trait, such as eye colour, but others control more than one trait, and some genes control the activity of many other genes.

Given that the main purposes of the genetic code and mechanisms of inheritance are to maintain the *status quo ante,* it follows that an animal or plant produces offspring that are almost identical to itself. If one looks at a small lizard, scuttling away when disturbed, one is looking a very long way back in time. These animals developed to a state which provided a very efficient organism, capable of flourishing in a wide variety of environments, a very long time ago. They have remained essentially unchanged for many millions of years. The wild horse of 5 million years ago was essentially the same as our present-day native ponies. The body form of sharks has remained unchanged for hundreds of millions of years.

Two different kinds of variation can be distinguished. These are continuous compared with discontinuous, sometimes called quantitative vs. qualitative. Continuous/quantitative variations occur in small steps over a wide range, with the majority of individuals close to the mean. Height in humans is an example. The discontinuous/qualitative variations lead to well distinguished groups that are clearly in one category or another, such as the human blood groups.

Changes leading to variation are mainly due to mutations. Mutations are random DNA copying errors that can take place at the time of cell division. Cells have efficient repair mechanisms to prevent these copying errors having an effect, but sometimes the repair mechanisms do not prevent the expression of a mutation. Mutations can occur in both somatic and germ-line cells. The number of spontaneous random mutations in somatic cells greatly exceeds the number of *de novo* mutations (DNMs) in germ-line cells. However, it is important to note that somatic mutations are not inherited. Many somatic mutations have very limited effect, although some can cause serious disease. It is only a mutation within a germ-line cell that can be transmitted to the next generation. The mutation itself is a change in a base pair in the deoxyribonucleic acid (DNA) of a gene. The genome is made of DNA which forms into a double spiral (the double helix of Watson and Crick). These helices are made up of very long strings of "bases". There are four different nitrogen bases in DNA. These are: adenine, cytosine, guanine and thymine. The order in which these bases are strung together forms a code: the genetic code. A personal computer operates with a binary code of plus or minus, which is one bit. The genome has a code of four variables.

A gene contains a large number of base pairs, and a mutation may consist of a change to a single base pair or to quite a large portion of the gene. A single gene may experience a lot of mutations of many different kinds, each of which could have a different effect. The complete human genome is made up of billions of base pairs. Most of the time copying of DNA during cell division (mitosis or meiosis) takes place without errors. Most mutations take place in the non-coding regions of the genome (the regions that do not code for protein production) so therefore have no effect: most of our DNA is non-coding.

As the role of mutations is of such fundamental importance to variation and therefore to the mechanism of evolution, it is worthwhile to think about how frequently mutations can occur in germ-line cells, and therefore how likely they are to produce a change in the next generation.

Gametogenesis follows a common path in human males and females, in the early stages, but later diverges along slightly different routes. It begins with the production of primordial germ cells in the dorsal endoderm of the yolk sac at about 10 weeks after conception. These cells proliferate and migrate in a posterior direction along the hind gut of the embryo to the gonadal ridge by about 20 weeks of gestation. There they multiply by mitosis to form the gametogonia, which are different in females and males. In the female these cells are primordial follicles, which number about one to two million at birth, and remain in the dictyate (a prolonged resting phase in oogenesis) until the start of menstruation. At each menstrual cycle a haploid gamete is produced by a process of mitotic and then meiotic divisions to produce an ovum. In the male, spermatogenesis begins at puberty and continues for the entire life of the testis. Mitotic and then meiotic cell divisions produce haploid male gametes (spermatozoa). Mutations in functional genes may often cause the egg and/or sperm to be non-viable.

So what opportunities do these processes give for the occurrence of mutations? In the early stage of gametogenesis, there is a lot of cell division, which would give many opportunities for mutation to take place. If a mutation took place at a really early stage, it would be reproduced in subsequent generations of germ-line cells and could be present in a high proportion of the eggs or sperms produced. Mutation at a later stage would mean that few of the eggs or sperm contained the mutation. Out of a potential million eggs, only about 400 (one a month for 13 months a year for about 30 years) are exposed to the possible opportunity of fertilisation. An ejaculate contains many millions of spermatozoa but only one is needed to fertilise the egg. So in both males and females, the chance of a mutation getting through to exist in the next generation may be quite small, depending largely on when it occurred. The maturation stage of the formation of the gametes only involves one mitotic and two meiotic cell divisions: only three opportunities for mutations to take place. Thus it appears that most mutations are likely to occur during the multiplication of the primordial germ cells, which is mainly in the second trimester of the mother's pregnancy.

At the final two stages in the production of gametes, where cell division is by meiosis, chromosomal crossovers take place. This is referred to as recombination. [Crossovers occur when two homologous chromosomes break and then reconnect.] Recombinations are random, controlled by their own set of genes. They are variable in frequency. It is a shuffling of genes which increases genetic variability. If two alleles differ, it may be important which one is kept in the chromosome that reaches the zygote. One may give better fitness than the other. But chromosomal crossovers can only rearrange existing genes, without affecting the nucleotide sequence: nucleotide sequence differences between members of a pair of alleles are due to mutations.

Another difficulty about the final expression of a mutation is of course the type of gene in which the mutation occurs. If the gene is dominant it will usually be expressed, but if the gene is recessive it will not be expressed unless its counterpart gene is damaged or absent. Usually recessive genes are only expressed when they are present in both of the parents.

Recent studies suggest that present day humans usually differ from their parents by about 30 germ-line DNMs. When you come to think about it, this is not many. There seems to be a paradox here between the large number of germ-line DNMs that would appear to be needed to produce the many complex changes seen during evolution, and the need for species to retain their identity by limiting the number and frequency of germ-line DNMs.

Consider an example of an evolutionary change. Palaeoanthropologists think that the key feature that identifies the start of the human lineage is bipedalism. Before the splitting-off of the human lineage, about seven million years ago, there were animals probably somewhat similar to present day chimpanzees. Some developed bipedalism to found the human lineage, the others continued to be quadrupedal and founded the various other primate lineages. Present day chimps have hind legs that are aligned vertically, going straight down from the hips, like the legs of a table. The human leg, which has become modified to become a very efficient walking machine, has a femur that is angled in towards the mid-line. At the same time, the tibia has become slightly angled outwards, so that the feet are next to each other and quite close together. The very well-preserved skeleton of the "Turkana boy" from 1.6 million years ago has legs very similar to present day humans, although his cranium is archaic. Bipedalism started several million years earlier than him. So to produce the human leg from the chimp style of leg would have required changes to the configuration of the hip joint and the knee. These would have affected surrounding muscles, tendons, nerves and blood vessels. The configuration of the hip joint must be controlled by large numbers of genes. The knee joint must be controlled by large numbers of other genes. This suggests that to bring about the structural changes associated with bipedalism would require mutations in many of these genes and these mutations would need to occur synchronously and in complementary modes. Even allowing for mutations in regulatory genes that can control large numbers of other genes, it would appear that large numbers of mutations were needed to do this.

But the explanation might not depend entirely on the sudden appearance of new mutations, but rather the selection of long existing mutants in some of the individuals, if the structural genes of the pelvis and legs showed some genetic variation that was additional to the phenotypic range that most traits show. Suppose that some of the ancient hominids happened to have legs that were slightly better suited to walking upright, due to the particular set of genes that they possessed. Then, supposing that those individuals *wanted* to walk upright, they would have had an advantage, and would have tended to out-live the others. If this process was genetic and therefore heritable, and was repeated many times over it could eventually arrive at the structural arrangement of the pelvis and lower limbs that we now have. It appears that the morphological change leading to bipedalism must have been preceded by a behavioural change because present day chimps sometimes walk on their hind legs, but only for a short time. If a change took place in the knee and hip of a chimp, which would enable it to walk on two legs more easily, it would not be selected for, because the chimp so seldom uses this mode of walking. It appears that the first change leading to the start of the human lineage was a change in mental attitude. Unlike other animals, which are not innovative, our earliest ancestors must have decided to try something new: to walk on their hind legs, for whatever reason, despite the difficulties of doing so, before the anatomical changes to the leg took place. Walking upright on two legs gave the advantage of greater height which enabled seeing predators or food from further away. When the leg did change to a configuration more favourable to walking, this would have been an advantage that would have been selected for. It was the mental attitude which led our ancient ancestors to make flint tools and later make purposeful use of fire. It was a mental attitude that caused sedentism and agriculture. Our development has always been led by our minds.

To take another example of adaptation, the famously long neck of the giraffe depends on there being some variation in neck length. Then the ones with longer necks can survive better, because they can reach up to eat the higher leaves. This is referred to as phenotypic variation around the mean. But phenotype depends on genotype. There has to be a difference in genotype for the longer neck to be inherited. Eventually there will be disadvantages in having a neck that is too long, so then selection for a longer neck will stop. The same applies to horses. The long neck of a horse enables it to graze the grass while still standing, despite its very long legs, so that it is in a position to run away immediately when a danger suddenly appears, but if the neck was too long it would cause imbalance and be a disadvantage.

All that genes can do is specify the production of proteins. A mutated gene might produce a different protein, or perhaps more likely a defective protein. To produce a useful evolutionary change in a structure or process a mutation would have to change the production of a structural substance or production of some controlling molecule, in a way that conferred an advantage in the owner's environment. Not all mutations would do that, but evidently some do. There must be many theoretically possible gene mutations that never occur. What is surprising is that mutations that turn out to be useful have kept on coming along. Why were there ever mutations that led to a feather, for example? Why did they ever happen?

Most if not all characteristics of a living organism show some variability around a mean figure. This "wobble" may be quite pronounced or very small. This is seen, for example, when a person has a blood test. When they see the results for the blood count, or for other factors such as Na^+ or K^+, they will see their own result, and next to it a range of "normal values", based on the results from hundreds of healthy people. Their result should fit into the normal range, but nobody knows what their own "normal" is, unless they have dozens of tests done at different times of day and varying circumstances.

Variation can also be caused by gene flow and by sexual reproduction, as well as mutations. Gene flow occurs when a population of a species interbreeds with another population of the same species, which leads to the transfer of genes from one population to the other. Sexual reproduction constantly introduces variation because the offspring receive a complement of genes from each parent. Some parental traits will show in the progeny, others will not. Sexual selection at mating leads to the evolution of showy traits which are useless for survival although they may result in more progeny.

It is important to understand that the variation seen in a trait can be genetic or phenotypic. Phenotypic differences are due to differences in many factors that bear upon the development of the individual. For example, the farrier's strong arms are a phenotypic change caused by muscular exertion. Phenotypic plasticity is a feature of the Extended Modern Synthesis which depends on one genotype being associated with more than one phenotype. A pair of identical twins (same genotype) could have different phenotypes with one being muscular and the other weakly, because one likes to work out in the gym but the other does not. At present, it is still generally believed that only genetic changes mediated by the gametes can be passed to the next generation, except for developments in epigenetics which are beginning to modify that view. Natural Selection and variation are important factors in evolution but recent work places more and more emphasis on the importance of molecular changes in genes as the driver of evolution.

Epigenetics

Epigenetics is the study of cellular and physiological phenotypic trait variations that result from external or environmental factors that switch genes on and off and affect how cells express genes, without a change in the nucleotide sequence of the DNA. A widely accepted definition of epigenetics was approved at a Cold Spring Harbor meeting in 2008: "Stably heritable phenotype resulting from changes in a chromosome without alterations in the DNA sequence."

A gene may be present in a more active or less active state. If it is active it can perform transcription, thus expressing itself. When geneticists talk about a gene being switched on or off, they mean that the gene is either expressing itself through transcription or it is quiescent and not expressing itself.

Transcription is the first action in gene expression. It consists of copying the nucleotide sequence of a particular segment of DNA to RNA, usually messenger RNA (mRNA) using the enzyme RNA polymerase. After that the RNA produces the corresponding protein by a process called translation. Reverse transcription can also occur, in which there is synthesis of DNA from an RNA template.

Changes in the transcriptional potential of a cell are not always heritable, but some are. Only those that can be inherited come under the heading of epigenetics.

There are three systems which are currently known to initiate and sustain epigenetic change, by altering transcription potential. These are DNA methylation, histone modification and ncRNA-associated gene silencing. [ncRNA = non-coding RNA] All of these activities can change how genes are expressed.

DNA methylation

In brief, the best-known DNA methylation process is the covalent addition of the methyl (CH_3) group at the 5-carbon of the cytosine ring, which results in the production of 5-methylcytosine (5-mC), which is so common that it is sometimes called "The fifth base of DNA". These methyl groups project into the major groove of DNA and inhibit transcription. In somatic cells, the majority of 5-mC is found where a cytosine nucleotide is located next to a guanidine nucleotide forming CpG. In most of the genomic DNA, the CpG sites are nearly all heavily methylated but in germ-line tissues many CpG sites are not methylated, allowing gene expression.

DNA demethylation is also an important process that operates in the reverse direction. It is involved with epigenetic reprogramming and many important disease processes including the progression of tumours.

There are complex biochemical pathways which control all these activities and one can only feel the greatest awe and respect for the wonderful way in which the whole system arose and that it works in such perfect harmony.

Histone modification

Chromatin is the complex of DNA and proteins that is packed within the cell nucleus. DNA is tightly condensed by being wrapped around nuclear proteins called histones. This produces chromatin. There is a repeating pattern of 146 base pairs of double stranded DNA wrapped around eight histone proteins. One such set is called a nucleosome. These repeating nucleosomes can be seen under the microscope and resemble a string of beads. The more condensed the chromatin, the harder it is for transcription to take place. Chromatin condensation can be changed by chromatin remodelling, caused by changes to the histone molecule brought about by methylation/demethylation and acetylation or deacetylation. This can alter the structure of the chromatin leading to transcriptional activation or repression. To clarify, changes to the histone molecule by, for example, methylation, will lead to changing the degree of condensation of the chromatin. More condensed chromatin reduces transcription (meaning that the effect of the gene is less obvious) and *vice versa*.

nc-RNA gene silencing

A non-coding RNA is a functional RNA molecule that is transcribed from DNA but does not translate into proteins. There are two groups of ncRNAs that appear to be involved in epigenetic processes, called "short" and "long". Both are involved with the formation of heterochromatin and with histone modification, DNA methylation and gene silencing.

Epigenetic changes can last for many cell divisions and several generations. Epigenetics can produce a change in phenotype without a change in genotype, although many epigenetic effects may make no difference to the phenotype. Epigenetic change is a constantly occurring, normal process. The frequency of epigenetic changes can be influenced by age, by environmental effects and by the effects of some diseases. Epigenetic changes are also thought to be responsible for the initiation of some diseases, including cancer.

Epigenetic change operates constantly during the process known as morphogenesis, that is to say the development of an embryo. The fertilised egg is known as a totipotent cell. It is a single cell which has all the information within it to make all the different cells found in the adult. Several pluripotent cell lines are derived from the original fertilised egg and these in turn produce fully differentiated cells, each of which can make one particular tissue, such as blood, nerves, muscle or bone. This is done by activating some genes while inhibiting the expression of others. The difference between, for example, a liver cell and a kidney cell is due to the different activation and suppression of certain genes.

Work continues to better understand and evaluate the importance of epigenetic inheritance as it occurs now, and the effect that it might have had upon the outcome of evolution over many millions of years.

4. The Brain

The human brain is large, both in absolute size and in size relative to body size. It weighs about three pounds (1.4 kg). There is an approximate relationship of body size to brain size in the higher animals, which can be plotted as a graph with most values lying on or close to a straight line. Brain size is not a simple percentage of body mass. It has been shown to increase as the 3/4 power of body mass. People are 7.5 units above the slope, much greater than any other animal. Much is made of this large brain size in a lot of the writing about human evolution, but this has been overemphasised. There are two aspects which we need to consider in some detail. These are, why did the human brain grow so large and what is the significance of a large brain in human evolution. Linked to these are questions about how the brain relates to thought and how does it carry out the complex cognitive processes, especially language and abstract thought, which set people aside from the higher animals.

Brain size

A mouse has a small brain, especially compared with a cow or an elephant. But a mouse can carry out all the same functions as the larger animals. It has just as much intelligence, in terms of its ability to deal appropriately and effectively with the events which occur throughout its life. Like other mammals, its essential behaviour falls into only a few categories. These are the essential abilities that all the higher animals, including the early hominids, must have to enable them to survive and prosper.

All the higher animals have the ability to carry out what is a fairly restricted set of requirements. They must be able to recognise danger and to act appropriately in response to danger. They have to be able to recognise what is wholesome food and what is not safe to eat. They must be able to identify their own species and a mate of the opposite sex. They need a limited degree of ability to nurture offspring. They can all do this, regardless of their size. So one might ask, why does an elephant have a larger brain than a mouse?

Part of the answer lies in the work the brain does to monitor and control a vast number of bodily processes, including the responses of proprioceptors throughout the body and the management of the eyes and other organs, which are larger in the larger animals. So its larger brain spends a lot of effort on housekeeping and sensory perception, not tied to intelligence. It is reasonable to suppose that a larger body requires more brain to carry out these processes. This is easily seen to apply to large animals such as whales and elephants, but the gorilla is no larger than a cow, so why should it have a larger brain than a cow, for housekeeping and sensory perception? Why did the primate brain get so much larger than was needed, either for thought or for control and surveillance of the body? There does not yet seem to be an answer to this question.

So the question remains, why should the human brain be so far above the normal slope. At this point, it must be remembered that there are disadvantages to having a large brain. The most obvious is that a larger brain requires more energy to operate. Also that a larger brain means longer nerve pathways—longer distances between different sections of the brain which need to communicate with each other. There are also potential obstetrical problems with the larger head that accommodates a larger brain.

Energy requirements

In very round terms, the present-day human brain is about 2% of the total body mass but it uses about 20% of the energy expended by the whole body. A smaller brain would use less energy, and this would be an advantage in many situations where food is in short supply. Suppose there was a man who rode a bicycle to work, but decided he would like to drive to work. He would be expected to buy a small car. If he bought a bus, and drove himself to work in that, he would be thought stupid to waste so much money on more fuel than needed. A process of natural selection would never do such a thing; it would select for energy efficiency. So the large human brain runs counter to what would be expected on grounds of energy consumption and Natural Selection.

Douglas Fox (1) has published a good summary of recent work that places physical constraints on the size and efficiency of a brain. Taking the example of the present brain of people, there are four principal ways in which it might theoretically be made more powerful: increasing size, increasing the number of neurons it contains, increasing the interconnectedness between different segments of the brain, or increasing signalling speed.

Increasing brain size would increase the number of neurons it contained, but would increase the energy it consumed. As it got larger, the axons that connect neurons would have to get longer, which would make them slower. If more neurons were packed into the existing space, the neurons or axons or both would have to be smaller. But if they get too small they tend to fire randomly: the signal to noise ratio is reduced. Adding more links between neurons enables parts of the brain to communicate more efficiently, but this uses up energy and space. Signalling speed could be increased by making axons thicker, but this would also increase energy demand and take up more space. Also, it has been observed that as brains become larger over time, the amount of white matter (axons) increases more than the amount of grey matter (neurons), meaning that there is more "wiring" relative to the number of synapses that do the processing.

Thus it seems that people's brains are not likely to get more efficient than they are now. The human brain seems to be optimally configured for efficiency relative to size and energy needs. One can only speculate about when the human brain reached this stage of efficiency: probably a couple of million years ago. But this does not explain how the primates did get to have such large brains. The brain of the gorilla is about one third the size (see below) of the present-day human brain but similar in gross structure to that of people. At the microscopic level, it can be seen that cortical neurons in primates enlarge very little as the brain increases in size, which is unlike most other mammals. A few neurons do enlarge, to carry out long distance signalling between different segments of the brain, but most do not. A doubling of brain mass between two different species of primates results in a doubling in the number of neurons, but a similar doubling of brain mass in rodents would only increase the number of neurons by 60%. However, data reported later in this chapter indicated that the rat brain, weighing four times as much as a mouse brain, had four times the processing power of the mouse brain.

Obstetrics

It has been said that a larger brain, in a larger head, can present problems when giving birth to a baby. This potential difficulty has been somewhat reduced because the rate of functional brain development in humans is relatively delayed compared with other mammals. But one might question the importance of a larger head in human obstetrics. Abnormal or difficult childbirth (dystocia) can be associated with abnormal performance of the uterus or abnormal lie or presentation of the foetus. A potentially fatal malpresentation is a breach birth, in which the baby is folded at the waist and tries to exit, doubled up. Normally the baby's head comes out first, but the shoulders can present a great obstacle to birth. Shoulder dystocia is where the head emerges but the shoulder is too large to pass through the pelvic canal. There are many obstetric manoeuvres designed to try to deal with this. About 20% of present-day human births are associated with some form of dystocia. Many of them require significant manipulation or other intervention to avoid death of the foetus, the mother or both. It is therefore likely that there were a lot of deaths due to dystocia in the ages before women received assistance at childbirth, but probably few of these would have been due to cephalo-pelvic disproportion (head too large), so the obstetrical disadvantage of a large brain may have been overstated.

Brain function

A few words need to be said about what the brain is, and how it works, but not in any detail in a book such as this. Much information is available in text books. Macroscopically the brain looks like a big lump of greyish jelly. Its gross structure has been well examined by anatomists and its fine structure by histologists. In recent decades, it has been possible to associate certain functions with different parts of the brain, using Functional Magnetic Resonance imaging. It has been found that most functions involve several parts of the brain at the same time. The brain consists essentially of two parts: the cerebellum with the brain stem and associated structures, and the cerebral hemispheres which lie above them. In very crude terms, the former do the mechanical chores and the latter do the thinking, including the production of visual images and auditory imaginings. The brain contains very large numbers of nerve cells (neurons): about 100 billion. These neurons have receptor fibres called dendrites at one end and an axon for outgoing impulses at the other. In the cerebral hemispheres, the neuronal cells are found in the grey matter, which forms a thin (3–4mm) layer on the outside of the brain. The larger part of the brain consists of the axons which connect neurons with each other. Some of them are long, sufficient to connect different areas of the brain together. These constitute the white matter. It is possible to detect electrical activity in the brain. The neurons produce electrical activity by a process involving the migration of ions through membranes. All this enables the brain to control body processes and to control muscular movements. It enables us to see, hear and smell things. Most importantly the brain appears to be the part of the body that facilitates thought. It is the link between our mind and our body.

Without going into too much detail on brain function, it may be helpful to our discussion to consider just one aspect of how one part of the brain carries out its functions. Let us do this by considering the activities of Purkinje cells, which well-illustrate the great complexity of the brain as known to us at present.

Purkinje cells are named after the famous Czech anatomist and physiologist Jan Evangelista Purkyne 1787–1869. Nowadays his name is written Purkinje. They are found in the cortex of the cerebellum. Purkinje discovered them in 1837, two years later also discovering the Purkinje fibres in the heart. He was a remarkable man of immense achievements. Purkinje cells are large globular neurons, with a large bunch of dendrites at one pole and a long axon at the opposite pole. Their function is to regulate muscular movements. They constitute 0.1% of cerebellar cells. They lie between the granule layer and the molecular layer of the cortex. The granule layer contains the very small granule neurons. The molecular layer contains only a few neurons, of two types: Stellate cells and Basket cells. Purkinje cells are called "projection neurons" because they have long axons which connect to other parts of the brain. Other types of projection neurons are excitatory, Purkinje cells are unusual because they are inhibitory projection neurons. They are the second largest cells in the brain (Betz cells are larger). They have an extensive dendritic "arbour" which is fan shaped, that is, flat, two dimensional, and the cells are stacked together "like dominoes". Neurons that connect over short distances are called "interneurons" and these may be either excitatory or inhibitory. The dendrites of the Purkinje cells generate "action potentials", but not in the same way as axons. Nerve axons produce action potentials by influxes of sodium ions. The action potentials in Purkinje dendrites are caused by influxes of calcium ions. The dendrites are furnished with spikes, which connect them to other cells. The Purkinje cell dendrites get their stimulation from two classes of cell. These are Granule Cells and Climbing Fibres. Granule cells make up half the total number of neurons in the brain. Each Purkinje cell receives input from up to about 200,000 parallel fibres, which are the axons of granule cells. The amount of stimulation they provide is weak. They are thought to control the overall sensitivity of the muscular movement control system. The Climbing Fibres originate in the area of the brain called the Inferior Olive. There is only one climbing fibre to each Purkinje cell, but it provides about 500 connections. It is thought that these Climbing Fibres control the extent and direction of muscular movements. The stimulation this provides is strong. Both Basket cells and Stellate cells provide inhibitory input to the Purkinje cells. Basket cells synapse on the cell bodies of the Purkinje cells. The Stellate cells connect to spikes on the Purkinje cell dendrites.

The cerebellum acts as an error-correcting mechanism, or more precisely a "pattern-recognition data processing system". When an action is performed, for example, picking up a pen, the cerebellum controls the accuracy of the movement. It compares inputs describing what you want to do, with what is actually happening and makes adjustments. The parallel fibres of the Granule cells continuously monitor this process and set the "gain" of the system. The Climbing Fibres become active when an error is detected. When the Purkinje cell is activated, it sends an inhibitory signal to a receptor cell, which then becomes inactive. The effect is mediated by release of a neurotransmitter called GABA (gamma-amino butyric acid). The Purkinje cells send inhibitory signals to the deep cerebellar nuclei. This is the only output from the cerebellar cortex, for motor coordination.

This brief overview gives some idea of the complexity of this part of the brain. However, it really only scratches the surface. Painstaking investigations have led to much more knowledge about the electro-physiology of Purkinje cell action, but it is far too complex to describe here. Despite all these known facts, a great question still remains. It is "How do Purkinje cells know that I want to pick up the pen, not wind my watch?" What is the mechanism that enables Purkinje cells to respond to a thought? The speed at which they act is truly amazing.

We have already considered the difficulty of understanding how action potentials in neurons can in some way become thoughts in our minds. This is something that is completely unexplained. Our thoughts are our most cherished reality. Your mind is what you are; more real to you than anything else, even the chair you are sitting on. The chair is mostly empty space. What you perceive as a chair is simply the mind picture that your brain makes for you, out of the various inputs it receives about the chair: the wavelength of light reflected from its various parts, its weight, the noise it makes if moved, the way it feels if touched, its smell. At the atomic level, it is a universe of particles and sub-particles separated by great distances. But your mind is you—really you. Nobody knows how it comes to exist. We are conscious, but nobody knows what consciousness really is. Now there is the other transformation. How does a thought cause a nerve cell in your brain to react? You have the pen in your hand and decide to write a word. The pen has to follow your detailed instructions about forming the outline of the letters. All this is done by the Purkinje cells—and very quickly too. But how do they get to know that you want to write an A and not a B? How does the material brain produce non-material thought? How does non-material thought cause the material brain to carry out a command. These are great mysteries to which there are no answers at the present time.

When Purkinje cells are damaged by heat stroke, incoordination follows. It has also been observed that Purkinje cells are smaller in the brain of autistic subjects, in whom there may be poor muscular coordination. As if that was not enough, it is thought that Purkinje cells are also involved with learning and some other cognitive functions.

Cerebral hemispheres as a heat shield

This leads us to the thought that the cerebral hemispheres may have enlarged because of their value as a heat shield. When our hominid ancestors decided to walk upright on their hind legs, one consequence was that the top of their heads became more exposed to sunlight. There were two elements to this. The posture of a quadruped, such as a dog or a horse, is such that the sunlight falls mainly on the back of their neck. When hominids became bipedal, the sunlight was no longer on the back of the neck, but on top of the head. Also, their heads were higher from the ground and therefore more exposed. It is thought that the start of bipedalism came at the same time as a migration out of the forest/jungle habitat and into the open savannah. If that is so, their heads would have been exposed to much greater heat from the sun, in Africa. Heat stroke can have seriously harmful consequences, especially for Purkinje cells, leading to motor incoordination. It may not be too unrealistic to suggest that individuals with larger cerebral hemispheres managed better, because the mass of cerebral brain tissue protected the cerebellum, brain stem, pituitary and pineal below from excessive heat. This could have led to a larger brain by a process of natural selection for the heat shield effect, which had nothing to do with the usefulness of the larger brain for processing purposes. It seems likely (see below) that the large cerebral hemispheres of a gorilla brain are hardly used for cognitive purposes: their thoughts are so simplistic that a very much smaller brain would have done. But the large brain produced in hominids became useful later on, when there was a requirement for complex spoken language and abstract thought.

The brain and computers

In thinking about our human brain, it is tempting to use the analogy with computers. This can be useful, although the analogy is not perfect. The brain represents the hardware of a computer, but it must also have pre-installed software programmes which deal with different activities. It is not possible to detect these programmes, any more than one could identify a computer programme by taking the machine to pieces and looking at the bits under a microscope. But they must be there. There must be programmes for dealing with the conversion of optic nerve impulses into a mind picture of the view ahead. It appears that children at a young age must have a language programme which enables them to deal so easily with complex grammar and syntax. All our higher intellectual abilities are likely to be facilitated by software programmes. It is the lack of such programmes in animals that explains their inability to speak a language or think in the abstract.

The development of computers has seen prodigious advances in recent decades. In about 1965, electronic calculators had reached a stage of development such that a machine about the size of a shoe box could carry out simple arithmetic calculations. Ten years later, the same mathematics could be performed on a calculator the size of a Credit Card. Moore's Law predicted that the number of transistors in computers would double every two years, for some time to come. This would mean a thousand-fold increase over twenty years. This has happened, together with the ability to get greater and greater performance into less and less space. This has been accomplished by remarkable increases in the efficiency of the subunits out of which the computers are built. This is a totally different situation to the human brain, where the increase in size has not been accompanied by any great change in architecture, or any miniaturisation, to pack more processing power into a smaller space. The physical structure of the human brain is likely to be much the same now as it was at the time of *Australopithecus afarensis* (Lucy).

Comparative aspects

At this point, it seems appropriate to write a few words about the present-day human brain compared with that of a chimpanzee. It is said that chimpanzees (*Pan troglodytes*) are our closest living relative. Sequencing of their DNA suggests a similarity with humans of about 98%. (Of course the 2% difference represents a lot of genes). Chimps inhabit Central and West Africa. Like humans the young chimps are very dependent in infancy and have a long childhood. They also have an opposable thumb. They seem equally at home swinging along the branches of trees or walking on all fours on land. Occasionally they will stand up and take a few steps in an upright position, walking momentarily on their hind legs only. They usually live in social groups of about 40 individuals. They mate every three years, the females being unable to conceive while nursing their young. Some studies have compared the cognitive ability of chimps with young babies. These tend to show that young chimps can perform the simplest tasks quite well, compared with human babies, but with more complex tasks the chimps are very far behind. In many cases, they simply have no idea how to do what the babies do easily. It appears that these differences are not due to the humans having a larger brain. It is due to the human brain being of a better quality at that time. Unlike chimpanzees, human brains have a very great increase in white matter during the first two years of life. This is a very important phase, in which the nerve axons make the connections to the grey matter, which will determine the efficiency of brain function. In humans from birth to teenage years, there is a fourfold increase in the volume of the human brain. During this time there is a great improvement in the quality of cognitive, perceptual and motor abilities. The delayed development of the human brain is thought to indicate that its development is more susceptible to the effect of post-natal life experiences, compared with other mammals. Life experiences appear to affect preferred neuronal pathways, perhaps rather like "burning" a CD.

Cranial capacity in cubic centimetres

A. afarensis	438	Lucy 3.2 m years ago
A. africanus	452	
H. habilis	612	
H. ergaster	871	Turkana Boy 1.6 m years ago
H. neanderthalis	1200–1900	0.2 m years ago

H. sapiens	1000–1900	average 1350 present day
Gorillas	340–752	present day

__Note__. It is difficult to measure cranial capacity accurately, especially with old specimens in which the cranium is incomplete. It has usually been done by filling the skull with small particles, such as mustard seeds. These are shaken down, and then tipped out into a measuring cylinder. The older figures given above are estimates based on this, and of course apply to individual specimens. More reliable data are available for the later human brains and Gorillas.

The cranial capacity of Lucy was about 438 cc. By the time of Turkana Boy it had become about 870 cc: approximately double. The cranial capacity of modern humans varies over a wide range from 1000 cc to 1900 cc with an average about 1350 cc. The smallest brains of today are not much larger than that of Turkana Boy, but the owners of these small brains are not handicapped by this.

Ralph L Holloway is a very distinguished professor of anthropology. He was one of the first to suggest that brain reorganisation occurred before the increase in brain size in hominids, which was an extremely important observation. He published (2) on the range of cranial capacity. He stated that the range of size of present-day human brains, from 1000 cc to 1900 cc shows no readily discernible correlation between brain size and behaviour. It is interesting that the cranial capacity of *H. neanderthalis* shows a similar wide range to *H. sapiens*, and especially since on average their brains were slightly larger than ours: another reason to suppose that brain size is not closely related to intelligence. In folk-law it is often the giant who is portrayed as being slow witted and the little man as being sharp witted, as for example the well-known French cartoon characters Obelix and Asterix.

Brain processing power

The human brain has enormous processing power. Neuroscientists are beginning to find out how great this is, and how it compares with computers and the brains of animals. The adult human brain is said to contain about 100 billion neurons and 1000 trillion synapses. (Of course there is a wide variation in brain size in humans, so this is just an approximation to mean brain size.) It is now thought that dendrites are more than simple connections; they may act as minicomputing devices for detecting and amplifying specific types of input, sorting impulses into different categories and actively processing received information, which would further enhance processing power. At present, the human brain is more powerful, much more compact and more energy efficient than any computer.

Neuroscientists have thought for some time that Brain Nerve Volume is proportional to processing power. Work on the human retina, published in 1998, attempted to calculate human brain processing power. The retina contains about 100 million neurons and seems to process about ten one-million-point images per second. The human brain, with a (mean) volume of about 1,500cc, is about 100,000 times larger than the retina. From this, by simple calculation it is possible to estimate the processing power of the average human brain as about 100 million MIPS. (MIPS = Million computer Instructions per Second.) That is about 10^{14} instructions per second. This was probably a considerable underestimate.

In 2007, studies were published that attempted to calculate the total computing power of all the computers and similar devices in the world. A daunting task which gave a figure of 6.4×10^{18} operations per second. At that time, this was said to be about the same as one human brain! It was also said that the total global information storage capacity at that time was about the same as the DNA in one human genome.

In 2013, studies were published in which a computer simulation was done using banks of processors that were thought to be equivalent to 1.73 billion neurons and 10.4 trillion synapses. Using this model it took a super computer 40 minutes to simulate one second of brain activity.

Studies by IBM, using 147,456 processors, were said to be able to simulate 4.5% of a human brain's activity. Note though, that this was in reference only to the thalamo-cortical part of the brain, not the whole brain, and also that the computers were digital, whereas the brain has analogue function. It was calculated that it would require 880,000 processors (similar to personal computers) to simulate the whole human brain. The simulations were not done in real time, but took about 600 seconds to represent one second. In the absence of any wiring diagram for the human brain, or detailed knowledge of its connectome, it is hard to judge what simulation means in this context.

The IBM neuroscientists were then able to carry out similar studies on some animal brains. They studied mouse, rat and cat brains and "were able to simulate the whole brain in each of these animals", using appropriate numbers of processors. However, all this work was heavily criticised by experts at the time. It was pointed out that the neuronal wiring diagram of none of these animals was known. The best that was known was a putative wiring diagram for a flat worm, with a total of 309 neurons. What should have been reported was that studies had been carried out using what were thought to be mouse-*sized*, rat-*sized* and cat-*sized* banks of processors. These were the figures (with brain weights added from other sources):

Mouse	512 processors	brain weight	0.49 g
Rat	2,048 processors	brain weight	2.00 g
Cat	24,576 processors	brain weight	25.60 g

Thus the processing power of these animal brains increased as the weight of brain tissue increased. If the proportionality of the actual brains to the supposed number of processors is correct, the fit of these figures of processors to weight is remarkable. The rat brain weighs four times as much as the mouse brain, and has four times the processing power. The cat brain is 12.8 times heavier than the rat brain and has twelve times the processing power. It is hard to assess the real importance of this work, but for the time being it may give some approximate idea of the relative processing power of the brains of these animals.

If that is true, it leads to consideration of the processing power of the Gorilla brain relative to the human brain:

Brain weight of Gorilla: 340–752 g Average about 546 g
Brain weight of human: 1000–1900 g Average about 1350 g

Therefore the Gorilla brain weighs less than half as much as the human brain. The human brain is two and a half times heavier in round figures. (Based on the ranges above the mean human brain weight is 2.47 times that of the mean Gorilla brain weight.)

From these figures, there arise some interesting considerations. Assuming that processing power *is* proportional to brain weight, it follows that the human brain has about two and a half times the processing power of the Gorilla brain.

This is a very small difference, insignificant in computer terms. But the cognitive and intellectual abilities of a Gorilla are many orders of magnitude less than a present-day person. In the everyday activities of life, eating, mating and such like, there is not much difference between a Gorilla and a person. It is in the intellectual function that there is so much that a person can do that a Gorilla cannot do at all. That is the enormous gulf between them and us.

A Gorilla has all the mental ability it needs to be a successful Gorilla, and the persistence of this species for millions of years shows that it did not need to be any more intelligent or capable than it is. The ancient hominids that lived cheek by jowl with the ancient Gorillas did not need to have any more brain power, either. They led very simple lives with few possessions.

One Gorilla has this staggering amount of processing power, equivalent to nearly one third of all the world's computers in 2007, but does nothing more with it than a mouse does with its much smaller brain.

The human brain is able to do all that the Gorilla can do, plus so much more: Language, Art, Music, Literature, Politics, Science, Philosophy, Theology, Conscience, and Worship of God. Our very complex language must use up a lot of processing power.

It would be simplistic to think that all that extra ability comes from a mere threefold increase in processing power. It cannot be that. It is obvious that the human brain has software programmes that enable these additional intellectual functions to operate. It is software that makes all the difference. If you want to write a letter, it has to be written on a machine that has word processing software. It would not matter how powerful your computer was, it will not write a letter unless it has a word processing programme installed. This is why the Gorilla cannot talk: it does not have the software for language.

Neuroscientists do not seem to say much about brain software. At present, it cannot be detected, but it must be there. There must be programmes in our brains that enable speech and language, and all the intellectual activities that people are capable of, in all their diversity and magnificence.

The limitation of neuroscience is that it examines the brain physically, much as one might dissect a television set or radio. This gives a clear picture of the components and their relationships, and it is possible to demonstrate the quiescent current flowing through the machines, and increased activity when they are receiving signals, but this approach can tell one nothing about the nature of the broadcast programmes being received. The detailed dissection of a computer will not demonstrate the nature of the installed software programmes. The great mystery of how the brain relates to thought remains unsolved and is likely to remain unsolved for a long time. Thoughts are not material objects: they have no mass or dimension. They are not detectable by any present day means. Brain activity seen on an electroencephalogram is an indication that the brain is alive and working, but tell us nothing about the thoughts (words) that are in the subjects mind at the time. Functional Magnetic Resonance Imaging can demonstrate areas of the brain that are active under certain circumstances, providing a link to cognitive activity, but do not read the thoughts (words) that are associated with the activity. Thoughts are associated with the brain and a brain is needed to generate thoughts, it seems, but how migration of ions through a membrane can become the most real part of a person's being is not known, and is difficult to imagine. Thoughts can also activate the brain and make it do things, for example the thought to write a word stimulating Purkinje cells as described earlier.

It is proposed in this book that the hominid brain has had unusual properties for a long time. It was a mental attitude that allowed the earliest hominids to become bipedal. It can only have happened because it was something that they wanted to do, as explained in another chapter. The hominid qualities of curiosity and inventiveness have been there a long time, leading to the first making of tools and the first use of fire. Going back long before that, the brain of Lucy, weighing 438 g, might have had a processing power about one quarter that of present-day people. She already had a mind significantly different from the animals around her. Our present-day brains may have only about twice the processing power of Turkana Boy. But it was not until quite recently that the human mind became the mind of a person, with all the wonderful abilities of abstract thought that we have. This sudden change, somewhere in the past 70,000 years, must have been a software acquisition. Software was installed into the human brain, to allow it to become the brain of a person. How this happened is not known, but the logic that it did happen is inescapable.

Our person's brain and the mind associated with it are unique. The ability to speak a language is unique. No other living thing on Earth can speak or understand a language. (For language think Virgil and Shakespeare, not grunts.) The ability of the present-day person's brain is so far removed from anything that is found in other brains, even those of similar size and structure, that it does represent a sudden, very large, departure from the normal. This is not characteristic of science in general or of Natural Selection in particular. It requires an explanation, and it is to theology that one has to turn to find an explanation.

The theological explanation is that the loving Creator made one living animal that could talk to him. This was the culmination of the creative process, leading to the existence of people who could speak God's language, to each other and to God. Everything else is subordinate to this. The natural world, so wonderful in so many ways, does point our minds towards God, but its primary purpose is to act as the foundation of the making of people. God loves all his creation, but it is people whom he loves most, and to whom he offers unconditional reciprocal love, to those who will accept it. For this, language is essential. That is why we have language. This is the complete and only answer to this question. The only reason that we exist is so that we can talk to God. That is why it is so important that we do talk to God. God listens to us all and it is right for us to tell God all about our lives, our hopes and our fears when we worship him.

Some people might say that it was impossible, because there is no scientific explanation at present. There probably is a scientific explanation of how it happened and how it works now, but the original event was one of the rare moments when God did something outside what is expected. God generally respects the scientific laws that he has created, only occasionally doing something that defies scientific explanation, at least in our present state of incomplete knowledge.

The way some writers refer to the huge increase in human brain size suggests that they are thinking of a many thousand-fold increase in processing power, but evidently this has not happened. It follows from this that it is a software difference which accounts for the difference in performance, not crude processing power. Of course, the relationship of brain size to processing power may be more complex. The brain can be seen essentially as in two parts: the cerebral hemispheres and the brain stem, cerebellum, pituitary and pineal glands. It is the cerebral hemispheres which took up the major part of the expansion in brain size. Even so, it seems unlikely that present day brain processing power is more than twice or three times greater than that of Turkana Boy or a Gorilla, representing an insignificant amount compared with the recent increases in computer processing power, and certainly not enough to explain the recent arrival of language and all the other mental attributes that combine to make the unique minds of present-day people.

References

1. Fox, D. (2011) *Scientific American*, **305**, 1, 36–43.
2. Holloway, R. L. (2015) 'The evolution of the Hominid brain', *From Handbook of palaeoanthropology*, **2**, 1961–87.

5. The Descent of Man

When Charles Darwin published *On the Origin of Species* (1) in 1859 he anticipated some controversy, following the vitriolic criticisms which followed the publication of the *Vestiges of Natural Creation* (2) in 1844, even though Robert Chambers made it clear in that book that he completely accepted that creation was the work of God. Despite these concerns, Darwin went on to publish *Variation in Animals and Plants under Domestication* (3) in 1868, which was concerned mainly with his ideas about inheritance, and then went on to publish the *Descent of Man* (4) in 1871. In the *Origin,* he said little specifically about the effect of Natural Selection on humans, but in the *Descent of Man* he said that he wanted to make up for this. In the Introduction, he wrote "The sole object of this work is to consider, firstly, whether man, like every other species, is descended from some pre-existing form; secondly, the manner of his development; and thirdly, the value of the differences between the so-called races of man."

He wrote a long book, which also included a lengthy second section on Selection in Relation to Sex. It is written with the characteristic clarity and detail for which he was already famous, and contains many interesting observations, and reports of observations by other naturalists. Darwin was determined that his theory of Natural Selection should be of universal application. He was worried that any exception to the rule would destroy the complete theory, so he made every effort to present all the arguments in favour of Natural Selection being the cause of the existence of man (meaning humankind, people) without the aid of anything else, as with all other species.

It might be said that his concern was mistaken, because making an exception of man would not have destroyed the value of his theory for all the other species. This is because people are so different in some respects from all other forms of life that it would not be surprising if additional elements were at work in our development. But Darwin refused to admit this, preferring to go to great lengths to try to show, by numerous examples, that man was not so very different from higher animals. In the *Descent of Man*, Charles Darwin clearly demonstrated that he believed that man was formed by a long and gradual process of evolution of the mind as well as the body. It is not entirely clear whether Darwin himself believed that this happened under the direction of God, but he probably did. It was his atheist admirers, especially Thomas Huxley, who took Darwin's work as support for their view that God was not needed. Robert Chambers had previously seen that all animate beings had arisen by a process of gradual development over a long period of time, but he saw this as the way in which the will of God had been expressed.

Darwin's concept of God must have been strongly influenced in his formative years by his two grandfathers, who held completely opposite religious views. Darwin's paternal grandfather, Erasmus Darwin, was a convinced and outspoken atheist but his maternal grandfather, Josiah Wedgwood was a Christian, fully committed to belief in God. It is hard to estimate how strongly Darwin believed in God. He wrote "The question is of course wholly distinct from that higher one, whether there exists a Creator and Ruler of the universe; and this has been answered in the affirmative by some of the highest intellects that have ever existed." Darwin exchanged letters with his wife Emma, who was a devout Christian (although a heretic as she did not accept the doctrine of the Trinity). In the letters, they discussed their belief in God. Emma may have regretted her husband's life and work being so fully committed to science and Darwin may have received support and reassurance in his belief in God through his wife's good influence. No doubt Darwin also wanted to avoid drawing upon himself the anger of the Church and the disapprobation of many of his friends, including some of the scientists, and the public at large, the great majority of whom were Christians. Darwin probably just wanted to write about his observations and conclusions regarding evolution and Natural Selection without being drawn into any religious controversy.

There need be no difficulty, nowadays, in accepting that the human body has developed in a way that generally follows the same path as other animals, up to the stage of the emergence of *Homo sapiens*. Darwin elaborated convincingly on that point, which he needed to do, in the climate of general opinion at that time. But for most people today there is ready acceptance of the view that humans developed from earlier forms in so far as our physical bodies are concerned. It is with the mental attributes that most people see such a large difference, both quantitative and qualitative, between present day people and animals, that they cannot be treated as the same. There are some mental characteristics of people that appear to be completely lacking in animals, as will be discussed later, although Darwin denied this.

Darwin did not recognise that there was a sudden change in the development of man: that it was not a steady climb over many thousands of years but occurred in step like stages, and that people today are very different from our ancestors of only 70,000 years ago. Of course in Darwin's day the recent pre-history of man was not known.

One thing which emerges clearly is that Darwin accepted the concept of inheritance of acquired characteristics. This is seen in many places in the *Descent of Man*. This is really quite remarkable, because the concept was so detrimental to the reputation of Jean-Baptiste Lamarck. He had recognised that the environment acted on individuals to bring about improvements, and very reasonably suggested the inheritance of acquired characteristics as the mechanism by which this happens. However his ideas were rejected by his contemporaries, for example his theory was dismissed, in the following terms, in *Vestiges*, page 230. "Early in this century, M. Lamarck, a naturalist of the highest character, suggested a hypothesis of organic progress which deservedly incurred much ridicule, although it contained a glimmer of the truth."

Darwin presented his theory of Natural Selection, without giving any suggestion as to how it actually worked. He attributed it mainly to widespread "variation", without explaining how this variation was generated. But he also believed in the inheritance of acquired characteristics as an important part of his theory.

There were great increases in knowledge about cell biology in the middle of the 19th century. Scientists, mainly in Germany, had excellent microscopes and they were able to visualise cells and describe cell division in great detail. They could see chromosomes, and they described the processes of cell division by mitosis and meiosis. These advances were a prelude to the work of Friedrich Leopold August Weismann (1834–1914), who is widely regarded as the most influential biologist of that century, after Darwin. Weismann developed his germ plasm theory. He said that inheritance can only operate through germ cells (gametes). Somatic cells (body cells) play no part in heredity. [This was before Mendel's work was widely known.] Germ cells produce somatic cells but are not affected by somatic cells. This led other scientists to speak of this as the Weismann Barrier. This has been generally accepted, but it is to some extent controversial, as some scientists think that there may be rare exceptions to the Weismann Barrier, in animals. In plants, things are rather different: because genetic changes in somatic cells of plants do result in changes in germ-line cells. The Weismann Barrier effectively put an end to the possibility of inheritance of acquired characteristics. This was of central importance to the Modern Evolutionary Synthesis.

To explain this further, the germ cells in mammals, including men and women, are made during embryonic development and are formed before birth. The DNA they contain is established long before birth, during the second trimester of the woman's pregnancy. Therefore the genome would not be affected by use and disuse of structures, leading to their strengthening or weakening, during the lifetime of the individual. However there is a recent increase in knowledge of epigenetics, in which it is postulated that some events can influence heritable characteristics without changes to DNA sequences, as discussed in another chapter.

Darwin firmly believed in the inheritance of acquired physical characteristics and also of acquired mental characteristics. His view of instinct, in the higher animals, was that it probably started as rational thought, applied to some activity. After several generations thinking in that way, it became "debased" (as he put it) to an instinct that was carried out without active cognition. It is hard to imagine how thoughts developed in a person's, or animal's, mind could influence the DNA already established in their gametes. Instinct remains a problem to understand, still awaiting an explanation.

It is evident that Darwin attached great significance and importance to the inheritance of acquired characteristics, because he went as far as developing a supposed mechanism by which it might work. He called this *pangenesis* and wrote a detailed description of how he thought this might work in *Chapter 27* of the *Variations of Animals and Plants under Domestication*. He could see that a mechanism was needed in which life events could influence the gametes. He postulated that minute, atom sized particles, which he called *gemmules*, were released from all body cells. [It is not without interest—as Robert Chambers would have written—that the word *gemmules* occurs in the *Vestiges*, on page 171, although in a completely different context.] Darwin postulated that the gemmules were affected by events, and migrated to the genital organs, where they aggregated and affected the gametes, before fertilisation. This process modified what was transmitted to the next generation. Thus events affecting cells could be passed on to the offspring, altering the information inherited. It w₁ cleverly thought out, but bears no resemblance to anything known to date in the natural world. However, in 2008, Y. Lin published an article "A new perspective on Darwin's pangenesis" (5) This has been followed by further publications by the same author on this theme, but it is difficult to evaluate the significance of this work at present. Showing the presence of nucleic acids or prions in sap or blood is one thing, but to demonstrate that they are capable of mediating the inheritance of acquired characteristics is altogether more difficult, and seems unlikely to be true.

Darwin did not include the description of pangenesis in the *Descent of Man*. His cousin Francis Galton carried out experiments with the original intention of providing evidence in support of pangenesis. He conducted a series of experiments between 1869 and 1871 in which he exchanged blood between rabbits of different colours, and showed that it had no effect on inheritance of their colours. Galton was disappointed and to some extent embarrassed by these results. Darwin dismissed these experiments as irrelevant: he said he had not postulated a role for the blood and would not listen to any criticism of his theory of pangenesis.

At this time, there was some controversy about inheritance of acquired characteristics, and in particular there were rumours that some Jews were born without foreskins, due to generations of circumcision. August Weismann carried out some experiments, designed to show the absurdity of this. He cut off the tails of 68 white mice, over five generations, and showed that none of their progeny had missing tails, or even shorter tails than usual. This is not an unexpected result, but it does raise the interesting question "How did humans lose their tails?" Not due to disuse, not due to injury, not due to thinking they were unwanted!

It is interesting to speculate upon how Darwin would have regarded his theory of Natural Selection if he had been forced to accept that inheritance of acquired characteristics did not happen. He might have had to accept the same criticism as given to Lamarck by Robert Chambers, in another quotation from *Vestiges*. "Now it is possible that wants and the exercise of faculties have entered in some manner into the production of the phenomena which we have been considering" [The development of higher forms of life from less developed progenitors.] "...but certainly not in the way suggested by Lamarck, whose

ᵱ   ᵑn is obviously so inadequate to account for the rise of the organic
                ᵗt we can only place it with pity among the follies of the wise."

            ᷄ Chambers was writing some years before Darwin published *The*
        ᵎ *of Man,* but later commentators should have used similar terms to
ᵈismiss Darwin's pangenesis. But they do not, usually just saying that it was
replaced by Mendelian inheritance, without saying that pangenesis was
unfounded. This is an example of the unfairness that can happen in scientific
writing: a lack of thoughtfulness on the part of some writers, or perhaps a lack
of integrity, because they want to support Darwin at all costs, regardless of any
weaknesses. Darwin still deserves the highest esteem for his brilliant
observations and writing on many subjects, and especially for his theory of
Natural Selection, but pangenesis was a totally wrong concept according to all
that is known now.

The book that Charles Darwin published in 1868: *Variation in Animals and
Plants under Domestication* was very large. Reading it now impresses by the
extent and depth of his observations on so many biological subjects. Darwin had
a great intellect: he must have had a wonderful memory for so many detailed
facts and a very efficient way of recording his own observations and those of so
many other naturalists. Most of his statements are backed up with references. His
industry and dedication to the task were so great; he must have spent an
enormous amount of time writing this book. There is now a website "Darwin on
line" which reproduces all Darwin's published work. The quantity and range of
this is really amazing, so much more than his major well-known works: *Voyage
of the Beagle, On the Origin of Species, Variation in Animals and Plants under
Domestication,* and *the Descent of Man.*

But the present-day reader may find *Variation in Animals and Plants* tedious
to read, and the admiration for it tinged with sadness. Here can be seen a great
mind at work, struggling to make sense of a multitude of disconnected facts,
trying to fit them into some kind of generalised theory of inheritance. This was
really an impossible task at that time, simply because there was not enough
known in those days about the way genetics work, at the molecular level. The
task could be compared with alchemists trying to understand the chemistry of
commonplace materials, in the ages before the atomic structure of matter was
known.

It is in this book that Darwin presents his theory of Pangenesis, and it is
evident that he could see that pangenesis, or something like it, was essential to

support his theory of Natural Selection. This is illustrated by the following excerpts from *Variation of Animals and Plants under Domestication:*

"How, again, can we explain to ourselves the inherited effects of the use or disuse of particular organs? The domesticated duck flies less and walks more than the wild duck, and its limb-bones have become in a corresponding manner diminished and increased in comparison with those of the wild duck. A horse is trained to certain paces, and the colt inherits similar consensual movements. The domesticated rabbit becomes tame from close confinement; the dog intelligent from associating with man; the retriever is taught to fetch and carry: and these mental endowments and bodily powers are all inherited. Nothing in the whole circuit of physiology is more wonderful. How can the use or disuse of a particular limb or of the brain affect a small aggregate of reproductive cells, seated in a distant part of the body, in such a manner that the being developed from these cells inherits the characters of either one or both parents? Even an imperfect answer to this question would be satisfactory."

This is such an important paragraph, perhaps the most important of all that Darwin wrote. The question he wrote is so well expressed and so good, and it remains unanswered, since Darwin's own answer—Pangenesis—is not true. Mendelian inheritance explains the way in which characteristics of parents are transmitted to their progeny. It does not allow inheritance of acquired characteristics, which is prohibited by the Weismann barrier and made impossible by the making of the gametes before the birth of their owner. But Darwin saw the need for inheritance of acquired characteristics, and evidently believed that this did happen, so he developed his theory of pangenesis to provide a physiological explanation. He did this by expanding very greatly on the observations given in the paragraph above, and went on to write:

"I have now enumerated the chief facts which everyone would desire to connect by some intelligible bond. This can be done, as it seems to me, if we make the following assumptions; if the first and chief one be not rejected, the others, from being supported by various physiological considerations, will not appear very improbable. It is almost universally admitted that cells, or the units of the body, propagate themselves by self-division or proliferation, retaining the same nature, and ultimately becoming converted into the various tissues and substances of the body. But besides this means of increase I assume that cells, before their conversion into completely passive or "formed material," throw off minute granules or atoms, which circulate freely throughout the system, and when supplied with proper nutriment multiply by self-division, subsequently becoming developed into cells like those from which they were derived. These granules for the sake of distinctness may be called cell-gemmules, or, as the cellular theory is not fully established, simply gemmules. They are supposed to be transmitted from the parents to the offspring, and are generally developed in the generation which immediately succeeds, but are often transmitted in a dormant state during many generations and are then developed. Their development is supposed to depend on their union with other partially developed cells or gemmules which precede them in the regular course of growth. Why I use the term union, will be seen when we discuss the direct action of pollen on the tissues of the mother-plant. Gemmules are supposed to be thrown off by every cell or unit, not only during the adult state, but during all the stages of development. Lastly, I assume that the gemmules in their dormant state have a mutual affinity for each other, leading to their aggregation either into buds or into the sexual elements. Hence, speaking strictly, *it is not the reproductive elements, nor the buds, which generate new organisms, but the cells themselves throughout the body*. These assumptions constitute the provisional hypothesis which I have called Pangenesis." (Emphasis added).

Darwin continued: "Before proceeding to show, firstly, how far these assumptions are in themselves probable, and secondly, how far they connect and explain the various groups of facts with which we are concerned, it may be useful to give an illustration of the hypothesis. If one of the simplest Protozoa be formed, as appears under the microscope, of a small mass of homogeneous gelatinous matter, a minute atom thrown off from any part and nourished under favourable circumstances would naturally reproduce the whole; but if the upper and lower surfaces were to differ in texture from the central portion, then all three parts would have to throw off atoms or gemmules, which when aggregated by mutual affinity would form either buds or the sexual elements. Precisely the same view may be extended to one of the higher animals; although in this case many thousand gemmules must be thrown off from the various parts of the body. Now, when the leg, for instance, of a salamander is cut off, a slight crust forms over the wound, and beneath this crust the uninjured cells or units of bone, muscle, nerves, etc. are supposed to unite with the diffused gemmules of those cells which in the perfect leg come next in order; and these as they become slightly developed unite with others, and so on until a papilla of soft cellular tissue, the 'budding leg', is formed, and in time a perfect leg."

Note. When Darwin wrote "supposed to", he meant "thought to" or "believed to".

Darwin went as far as to write "It is not the reproductive elements which generate new organisms, but the cells themselves throughout the body." He wrote "My gemmules are supposed to be formed quite independently of sexual concourse, by each separate cell or unit throughout the body, and to be merely aggregated within the reproductive organs." He believed that there was retention of free and undeveloped gemmules in the body from early youth to old age, admitting that it might seem improbable, but pointing out the way that seeds lie dormant in the earth for long periods. Darwin combined all these ideas together to make a theory of inheritance that was not correct and which runs counter to all that is now known about inheritance. But Darwin was right to think that some form of inheritance of acquired characteristics was greatly needed to enable the process of Natural Selection to work effectively.

That is the critical point for us today; that Darwin could see that the inheritance of acquired characteristics was needed to enable Natural Selection to work, in a helpful way and in a realistic time frame. That is why he invented and committed himself to pangenesis and promoted the idea so strongly and with such determination. Without anything like this Natural Selection struggles to account for macro-evolution in the time available. Why has nobody said this? Natural Selection is still a good idea, but its author has now lost the chief plank on which it could be thought to carry out its functions. This is not a criticism of Darwin, but of present-day writers. Darwin could not be expected to know about the mechanisms of inheritance which were not discovered until later. But present-day writers should not ignore the fact that Darwin was under an illusion about the way inheritance (of acquired characteristics) works, and that his trust and confidence in the inheritance of acquired characteristics was completely misplaced. This does weaken his theory of Natural Selection. The theory requires something to take the place of inheritance of acquired characteristics to make it work as well as it needs. Perhaps in time epigenetics will fill this gap.

It is the mental differences between people and animals that was then, and still is, controversial. Darwin devoted a lot of effort in trying to show that the higher mammals, and especially the primates, did show evidence of many of the same mental characteristics as we see in people today. He dealt with this under a number of headings, and we will look at these, and comment on them, one by one. But in all cases, what he was demonstrating were merely the rudimentary forms of thinking, which remained undeveloped in animals, but increased so enormously in people. It was rather like saying that a skate board is the same as an aeroplane, because both are a means of transport, without acknowledging that the aeroplane is very much more complicated. While disagreeing with Darwin's attempt to exactly equate animal minds with people's minds, it has to be recognised that people do have some mental characteristics that are derived from our ancient animal origins. Notable among these are our selfish responses, which reflect the animal instinct for self-preservation, without the moderation provided by our conscience which allows us to distinguish right from wrong. Higher animals do show some behavioural characteristics which are similar to those seen in people, but to a very much lower degree.

Darwin wrote under the following headings:

Mental powers. In Chapter 2, Darwin makes the comparison between "…the mental powers of man and the lower animals." He does admit that the difference in mental power is very great. "…the difference in this respect is enormous, even if we compare the mind of one of the lowest savages, who has no word to express any number higher than four, and who uses hardly any abstract terms for common objects or for the affections, with that of the most highly organised ape."

Darwin had much less contact with the "savages" than Wallace, who lived closely with the indigenous people in both South America and in the Malay Archipelago, for a number of years. Darwin wrote "I was constantly struck with surprise how closely the three natives (Fuegians) on board H.M.S. 'Beagle', who had lived some years in England, and could talk a little English, resembled us in disposition and in most of our mental faculties." The view Darwin took of such people, in common with most educated Englishmen at the time, was very demeaning, unlike today. Wallace had much more respect for them and a much clearer idea of the high level of mental qualities that were present in the most simple of societies, from his personal experience of living amongst them.

Instinct. In Darwin's day, there was some controversy regarding the existence of "instinct". In this chapter Darwin wrote "As man possesses the same senses as the lower animals, his fundamental intuitions must be the same." He goes on to say "Man has also some few instincts in common, as that of self-preservation, sexual love, the love of the mother for her new-born offspring, the desire possessed by the latter to suck, and so forth. But man, perhaps, has somewhat fewer instincts than those possessed by animals which come next to him in the series." This is true. Darwin digressed to speculate on the way instinct develops and its relationship with intelligence and rational thought. He points out "...man cannot, on his first trial, make, for instance, a stone hatchet or a canoe, through his power of imitation. He has to learn his work by practice; a beaver on the other hand, can make its dam or canal, and a bird its nest, as well, or nearly as well, and a spider its wonderful web, quite as well, the first time it tries as when old and experienced." Darwin thought that useful ideas are inherited but there is no known mechanism for this.

Emotions. Continuing, he wrote "...the lower animals, like man, manifestly feel pleasure and pain, happiness and misery...The fact that the lower animals are excited by the same emotions as ourselves is so well established, that it will not be necessary to weary the reader with many details." This is true, but only to a degree. The quality and intensity of the feelings of the lower animals is hard for us to estimate, but it is highly probable that they are less intense than in people. The reason for thinking this is that our complex language, and our ability to think of the past and the future, gives us the ability to add greatly to the intensity of any emotion, perhaps especially those concerning fear, pain or regret. Darwin's attitude to this is typical of his whole thesis: to show that there are some similarities between man and animals, then to imply that these similarities indicate identity. They do not: it is the differences that are the more important.

Intellectual emotions. Darwin wrote: "Animals manifestly enjoy excitement, and suffer from ennui. All animals feel *Wonder*, and many exhibit *Curiosity*." This may well be true, but as pointed out previously, the degree of these things is very different in people. Curiosity is greatly lacking in most animals. Darwin gave no examples to support *Wonder*, but gave the example of monkeys, who were frightened of snakes, overcoming their fear because of their *Curiosity*, which led them to take a quick look in a bag, containing a snake, before running away. However, until they looked in the bag they did not know it contained a snake, so fear did not have to be overcome. It seems that this example demonstrates not so much curiosity as reason. The monkeys may have noticed food being removed from bags, and were motivated to look in the bag for food. Finding food is the main preoccupation for most animals, most of the time. It is the high level of curiosity, leading to inventiveness, which is so characteristic of people and is one of the minor, but none the less important, features which distinguish us from all other forms of life. Animals generally remain content with what they have; they are not curious to improve anything.

Imitation. Darwin said that this is strong in man. He gave the example in animals of a dog, which had been brought up with a cat and kittens, and had learned to lick its paws in the manner of a cat.

Attention. Very important in man, but also seen in animals, Darwin gave the example of a cat watching a mouse hole, ready to spring when the mouse emerged.

Memories. Darwin states that animals remember persons and places. He related this ability mainly to domesticated dogs, which may not be regarded as entirely typical of all the higher mammals.

Imagination. Darwin said this was "one of the highest prerogatives of man." He wrote "As dogs, cats, horses, and probably all the higher animals, even birds, have vivid dreams, and this is shown by their movements and sounds uttered, we must admit that they possess some power of imagination." There is poor evidence for dreams and no evidence for "vivid" dreams. But it might be said that the nature of a dream is different from that of imaginings that take place in the wakeful mind. In a dream, certain images are presented, without being summoned, and there is usually little opportunity to modify them. They are often "remembered" real experiences. Perhaps a dog might dream about chasing a rabbit, but that would not be an example of imagination but of recollection. When imagining something while awake, there is a creative process, which builds up an imaginary situation or structure, based largely on the use of language. The imagination of gifted story tellers such as Emily Bronte, Dorothy Sayers, Miguel de Cervantes or Charles Dickens is so immense that to compare it with the possible dreams of animals is not an acceptable observation.

Reason. "Of all the faculties of the human mind it will, I presume, be admitted that *Reason* stands at the summit. Only a few persons now dispute that animals have some power of reasoning." Note: he said "some power." He continues "…the more the habits of any particular animal are studied by a naturalist, the more he attributes to reason and the less to unlearned instincts." He comments further "It is often difficult to distinguish between the power of reason and that of instinct." The examples he gave, in support of reason, show that animals do have some powers of reason, but Darwin seems unconcerned that there is such a massive gulf between the degree of reason exhibited by people and animals. He showed that a monkey and a pike (fish) both learned from unpleasant experiences, but that the monkey learned much more quickly. He went on to state "If we attribute this difference between the monkey and the pike solely to the association of ideas being so much stronger and more persistent in the one than the other, though the pike often received much the more severe injury, can we maintain in the case of man that a similar difference implies the possession of a fundamentally different mind?" Not perhaps fundamentally different: the fundamental plan on which the mind of both man and animals is based may be common to both, but the difference is that in man the mind progressed far beyond anything found in animals, and far beyond what was needed for the efficient conduct of man's life at that time. So Darwin tried to show a long and gradual progression from the pike to the monkey, and on to man, not recognising the huge leap from monkey to man, in a short period of time, compared with the lesser gap between the behaviour of the pike and monkey, which embraced enormous differences in organisation, from a fish to a mammal, and a vast passage of time. It may be wrong, in any case, to refer to the "mind" of a fish. It is likely that at their level, reactions to pain, as in this example, would be purely reflexes, not involving a thinking mind.

That man has a "fundamentally different mind" is demonstrated by other characteristics: language, conscience and belief in God, although Darwin denied these, as we shall see later. Darwin never mentioned the soul, which is, of course, the greatest of all the many distinguishing features of people.

Darwin went on to write a remarkable passage: "It has I think, now been shown that man and the higher animals, especially the Primates, have some few instincts in common. All have the same senses, intuitions, and sensations—ones, such as jealousy, suspicion, emulation, gratitude, and magnanimity; they practice deceit and are revengeful; they are sometimes susceptible to ridicule, and even have a sense of humour; they feel wonder and curiosity; they possess the same faculties of imitation, attention, deliberation, choice, memory, imagination, the association of ideas, and reason, though in very different degrees." But it is not true to say that "All have the same senses...they possess the same faculties..." There are similarities, but there are great differences in both the quality and extent of these similar feelings and faculties. Similarity is not identity. Showing all these similarities, as Darwin did, does not advance his cause at all, because a small similarity is meaningless set against the great size of the differences. In the paragraph above, some words should be left out altogether, for example: intuition, gratitude, magnanimity, sense of humour, wonder and imagination. A dog might be very happy to be given a warm bed and a good feed, but can it be said to feel gratitude? That is a complex emotion dependent on ideas about giving and deserving, sacrifice and love. It is likely that the emotion of gratitude is too dependent on language to be within the understanding of any animal.

It is remarkable that in *Vestiges,* page 335, Robert Chambers writes about the mental qualities of the higher animals in a way that closely resembles the way Darwin wrote, two decades later: "Common observation shews a great general superiority of the human mind over that of the inferior animals. Man's mind is almost infinite in device; it ranges over all the world; it forms the most wonderful combinations; it seeks back into the past, and stretches forward into the future; while the animals generally appear to have a narrow range of thought and action. We see animals capable of affection, jealousy, envy; we see them quarrel, and conduct quarrels, in the very manner pursued by the more impulsive of our own race. We see them liable to flattery, inflated with pride, and dejected by shame. We see them as tender to their young as human parents are, and as faithful to a trust as the most conscientious of human servants. The horse is startled by marvellous objects, as man is. The dog and many others show tenacious memory. The dog also proves himself possessed of imagination, by the act of dreaming."

Returning to *The Descent of Man* Darwin continued: "The individuals of the same species graduate in intellect from absolute imbecility to high excellence. They are also liable to insanity, though far less often than in the case of man." This seems a surprising statement, not required in making the case, and probably not true regarding intelligence. There are likely to be varying levels of intelligence in animals of the same species, but they are in a way superficial differences. They are the fine tuning of the intelligence: small differences that are not of practical significance. All the individuals are capable of living the life of their species efficiently.

His paragraph continues: "Nevertheless, many authors have insisted that man is divided by an insuperable barrier from all the lower animals in his mental faculties. I formerly made a collection of above a score of such aphorisms, but they are almost worthless, as their difference and number prove the difficulty, if not the impossibility, of the attempt. It has been asserted that man alone is capable of progressive development; that he alone makes use of tools or fire, domesticates other animals, or possesses property; that no animal has the power of abstraction, or of forming general concepts, is self-conscious and comprehends itself; that no animal employs language; that man alone has a sense of beauty, is liable to caprice, has the feeling of gratitude, mystery, etc.; believes in God, or is endowed with a conscience." How Darwin can say these are worthless aphorisms, can only be explained by his determination to prove his point, which distorted his usually sound judgement. In fact, the points Darwin listed above are all true, and all underline the difference between animals and people. Of course, Darwin was tending to think in terms of comparing "the lowest savage" with "the highest ape". That does reduce the differences by a fraction, perhaps, but the really meaningful comparison is between the generality of educated people and the generality of the higher animals (mammals).

The difference between people and animals is a theme taken up by Raymond Tallis in his important book "Aping Mankind", published in 2011 (6). He wrote a splendid book, presenting his arguments with clarity, authority and some flashes of humour. His main concerns were to deplore what he called *Darwinitis* and *Scientism*, that is the delusion that Darwin's theory of Natural Selection can be applied to everything and explain everything, and the mistaken belief that the natural sciences can and will give a complete description and even explanation of everything, including human life. Tallis devoted many pages to showing that present day humans, though coming from an animal background, are totally distinct from animals in so many Important ways that they must be regarded as completely separate, as already discussed in this chapter.

This is an idea which should be obvious to anyone, yet the view that people and animals are essentially the same has persisted, and in recent years has been amplified. Tallis points out that this belief has a long history, but it was Darwin, in *The Descent of Man,* who gave the greatest impetus to this wrong idea. Tallis points out that the proponents of this idea have developed two strategies in their arguments. These are animalising humans and humanising animals. He gives many good examples which show how the assumptions on which animalisation and humanisation are based are wrong. For example, he points out that it is wrong to describe a dinner party of people and a chimpanzee reaching out for a banana as equal instances of "feeding behaviour", ignoring the vast difference in complexity between the two. Likewise he contrasts someone signing up to do an evening course, to improve their career prospects, with Daisy the cow bumping into an electric fence and therefore learning not to do it again. Both are "learning behaviour" but of immensely different complexity. He points out too, that human learning is "deliberate, explicit, mediated through innumerable intermediate steps that require us to know what we are doing and why. What is more, our learning often depends on others to teach us. We are the only animals who deliberately instruct each other." Again, he wrote "A word such as 'courtship', for example, is transferred from the complex setting of the interactions between self-conscious human beings in a community of minds to the hard-wired behaviour of animals: the standardised pre-mating feeding rituals of herring gulls, for example."

In making the case, Raymond Tallis places great weight on the concept that people are very sociable, living in an extremely complex society, which is way outside anything that animals experience, even the most sociable of them. Consider the interest shown by so many people in society magazines and gossip columns, and now in the social networking sites on the internet.

During an interview to discuss his book at the time it was launched, Tallis is reported to have said "To see the difference between humans and animals, think about what you did yesterday, and what your dog did yesterday." This was a brilliant way of illustrating the great gulf between people and dogs, but it might be added, "Especially if yesterday was a Sunday and you went to Church."

Another marked difference between people and the higher animals is with regard to sexual activity. People make love with each other, animals do not do this, as Tallis points out. People, alone, think about wanting to give pleasure to their sexual partner. With animals, it is usually a matter of the male checking that the female is receptive (on heat) and if she is, mating with her, and if she is not, wandering off. In animals, there is usually no foreplay and sexual contact does not last for long. People generally try to do better than that.

In women, signs of heat have completely disappeared and one can only speculate about why this has happened. It might be a case where Natural Selection *did* come into play, because a woman who was always receptive to mating would be more likely to keep a man with her, which would have given her greater protection and support with greater survival potential. But it is curious that only the primates (and rabbits, guinea pigs, mice and rats) have haemochorial placentae. It is this kind of placentation that causes women's monthly menstruation, which causes a temporary loss of sexual activity. Of course the great advantage of haemochorial placentation is that it allows IgG antibodies (but crucially, not IgM) from the mother to enter the blood stream of the foetus, before birth, providing some immunity to some infections. The more separated placentation of a cow (epitheliochorial) for example, means that the calf is born without any antibodies: it depends on colostrum (the antibody-rich first milk) for its supply of antibodies to environmental pathogens. This is very effective if all goes well, but it depends on the mother being alive and producing plentiful colostrum and the calf having the ability and opportunity to suck, soon after birth, so it is a less secure system than that of humans where the foetus is born with a supply of antibodies already in its blood. The disadvantages of a haemochorial placenta, apart from the severe pain of dysmenorrhoea suffered by some women, are the monthly loss of blood, which requires extra food to support the making of new blood and also the increased difficulty of protecting the foetus from immune rejection by its mother, because of the closer connection with maternal blood than in endotheliochorial or epitheliochorial placentae. The mechanisms that are present to prevent the mother rejecting her foetus are fascinatingly complex. The foetus is not genetically identical to its mother, so it is potentially liable to be rejected in a kind of "host versus graft" reaction. This is (usually) prevented, and it is truly wonderful the way in which things like this happen: the orchestration of several different control mechanisms working together in harmony. So it is not clear cut that, overall, the haemochorial placenta provides better survival value to either the mother or her child.

But the haemochorial placenta is with us, which raises the thought that perhaps many new attributes arise and persist, even though they do not give greater survival value. It is when something changes for the worse that it is likely to be eliminated by Natural Selection, but positive selection is likely to be less frequent. The majority of developmental changes may happen, and not be modified much, or at all, by Natural Selection. Of course, Natural Selection does nothing to give rise to new characteristics, it is simply the action of the environment, in the widest sense, sparing certain individuals who are better adapted to their situation. The development of new characteristics depends on supposedly random changes in the genome. The possessor of the new characteristic has simply to make the best use they can of it, in the struggle for continued life.

What is especially interesting from the view point of a Christian is that Raymond Tallis is "proudly atheist". For a Christian, or most other religious believers, there is never any doubt that people and animals are different, because people are made in the likeness of God and have a soul. It is generally believed that animals do not have a soul. But Tallis does not use that argument. Furthermore, believers in God hold that people have two main duties: to worship God and to help other people. Humanism is very good at supporting the latter, but does nothing to support the former. There is some irony in a man setting out to prove that people are different from animals, but not acknowledging that one of the most important distinguishing features is that most people believe in God (whether their particular beliefs are right or wrong, they understand the concept of God), believe in the importance of worshiping God, and have a conscience that enables them to distinguish between right and wrong: all things that are completely absent in animals and plants. But the atheism of Raymond Tallis does strengthen the weight of the views he expresses, in general, especially no doubt in the eyes of other atheists, because he is not writing with a view to supporting a Deistic philosophy. Of course people who do not believe in God still understand the concept of God, and they have a soul and a conscience, although this is not explicit in his book, but Raymond Tallis has performed a great service to clear thinking by demolishing the idea that there is no difference between people and animals.

To reduce the criticism of Darwin for trying to show that people and animals are the same, it might be said that at the time he was writing his books the differences were slightly less obvious than now, because in those days most people led such simple lives, even in England, without the subsequent technology that now we all use. No cars, aeroplanes, personal computers, electric light, domestic appliances such as washing machines, tumble driers, electric cookers, and vacuum cleaners, no central heating, no telephones or mobiles, no radio or television or cinema. No ready meals or processed foods and little mass entertainment such as football matches. Their working lives were also much more simple, in general, than they are now with most men and women performing rather unskilled manual work. But the most important differences between people and animals were there, the language, the conscience, the soul and the belief in God: Darwin must have known this but it seems that he disregarded it to support the universal application of his theory.

Before leaving, this subject it is very important to stress that by asserting that people are distinct from animals does not in any way diminish the love and respect that people should show to the natural world and especially to the higher animals. We all have a duty of care towards the world we live in and to the animals who share it with us. Hardship or cruelty to animals must always be condemned in the strongest terms. Much more needs to be done to improve standards of animal welfare, world-wide.

When animals are kept in unnatural conditions of overcrowding and intensivism, their individual personalities are not so evident, but when treated as individuals they show many characteristics that indicate their awareness, perception and personality. Even a chicken, kept in back-yard conditions, will develop individual habits appropriate to its surroundings. The higher animals are all capable of pain, fear and distress and domesticated animals should be managed with the highest possible standards of animal husbandry and welfare.

Morality. Darwin wrote much more in The Descent of Man about the development of morals and conscience. He attempted to show that morality would develop by Natural Selection acting on man's "sympathy" for his fellow men and his practical realisation that cooperation with others is better than conflict within the group. So it seems that Darwin thought that there was no need to invoke a Divine origin for conscience. But what Darwin was talking about was the way in which morality developed, *after* man had developed a powerful brain and intellect. The question, of course, is how (and why) did that intellect develop in the first place. Why in man and not in the apes, who began from the same starting point as man, when the ancient lines divided over seven million years ago.

The modern reader can gain much pleasure and interest from reading *The Descent of Man*, with its large number of unusual, sometimes amazing and often amusing observations of animal behaviour. But it must be remembered that Darwin was trying to use *The Descent of Man* to disseminate his view that Natural Selection was solely responsible for the evolution of all living things, including humans and present-day people. As a young man Charles Darwin showed great determination and resilience in his voyaging and his writings. As an old man, in poor health, his determined nature turned chiefly to doing all that he could to ensure that his legacy of Natural Selection was accepted as a complete explanation for the development of all life, including people. *The*

Descent of Man was the result. Cleverly thought out and well-constructed though his arguments are, they do not convince, because the differences between people and animals are too great to be ignored or brushed to one side. Leaving aside the metaphysical points, such as soul and mind, the fact that only people have a spoken and written language sets us completely apart from all other living creatures.

To conclude this chapter let us look at the following quotation: "Man in the rudest state in which he now exists is the most dominant animal that has ever appeared on this earth. He has spread more widely than any other highly organised form: and all others have yielded before him. He manifestly owes this immense superiority to his mental faculties, and to his social habits, which lead him to aid and defend his fellows, and to his corporeal structure. Through his powers of intellect, articulate language has been evolved; and on this his wonderful advancement has mainly depended. He has invented and is able to use various weapons, tools, traps, etc., with which he defends himself, kills or catches prey, and otherwise obtains food. He has made rafts or canoes for fishing or crossing over to neighbouring fertile islands. He has discovered the art of making fire, by which hard and stringy roots can be rendered digestible, and poisonous roots or herbs innocuous. These several inventions, by which man in the rudest state has become so pre-eminent, are the direct results of the development of his powers of observation, memory, curiosity, imagination, and reason."

That is true, but only a low degree of the development of these qualities would have been enough to equip primitive people to perform the tasks that they learned to do. Even a low degree of development of intellect did not occur in other species. Darwin went on to write that "I cannot, therefore, understand how it is that Mr Wallace maintains that, 'Natural Selection could only have endowed the savage with a brain a little superior to that of an ape.'"

He could not understand, or would not understand? The reason is that Natural Selection depends on need. There has to be a need for a characteristic before it will be selected for, in preference to other characteristics. Darwin, of course, knew this better than anybody—it was his great idea. He explained it in *The Descent of Man* and elsewhere in his many writings. Wallace knew this too, but he also understood clearly what Darwin refused to acknowledge: that people have a mind, an intellect, far greater than was needed by the aboriginal people who possessed it, and greater in fact than most people need today. There was not a need for this overdeveloped intellect. Humans could have survived perfectly well with a lesser intellect. Our minds are better than we need, so they did not develop through Natural Selection. This is the point that invalidates Natural Selection as the maker of people from humans. No wonder Darwin would not accept it, even though it does not reduce the validity of Natural Selection for the other forms of life.

References

1. Darwin, C. (1859) *The origin of species by means of natural selection: or The preservation of favoured races in the struggle for life*, London: John Murray.
2. Chambers, R. (1844) *Vestiges of the Natural History of Creation*, London: John Churchill.
3. Darwin, C. (1868) *Variation in Animals and Plants under Domestication*, London: John Murray.
4. Darwin, C. (1871) *The Descent of Man*, London: John Murray.
5. Lin, Y. (2008) 'A new perspective on Darwin's Pangenesis', *Biol. Rev. Camb. Philos Soc*, **83,** 2, 141–9.
6. Tallis, R. (2011) *Aping mankind*, Durham: Acumen Publishing.

Part Two

In the first part of this book, we thought about the way in which people had tried to understand the physical world we live in and especially how it had developed and diversified over long periods of time. We recognised the contribution of many generations of scientists and theologians who have studied this. We saw that science and theology have different approaches to these studies and use completely different methods to pursue them. The emphasis was on the origin and development of the physical world while acknowledging that there is also a non-material (spiritual) world that is just as real as the physical world, and ultimately more important than the physical world because it is not subject to decay.

In the second part of this book, we will first consider the non-material world. We will then look at what the Bible says about people and the physical world and how that matches what we have been taught by science. This means a study of the archaeological material record of human development with the recent and sudden appearance of people. From this, it is possible to develop a combined theological and scientific approach which shows the most probable developmental pathway in the light of scientific observations and Biblical writing.

6. The Non-Material World

Why do people believe that there is a spiritual world just as real as the physical world that we can touch and see, even though science has no means of detecting it? The answers to this question fall into two categories: The perceived *need* for a spiritual world and the *evidences* that are around us that point to a spiritual world.

The starting point must be that we believe that God is everlasting. This means that God must be a spiritual being, not a physical being, as all things physical will decay. It is believed that God created Heaven, a spiritual world which is home to angels and is necessary for us to have a place to enjoy an everlasting life, after physical life has ended. We believe that we are spiritual beings, linked temporarily to a physical body. Only God could have given us this soul which gives us our immortality. These are the basic assumptions of all three of the Abrahamic religions: Judaism, Christianity and Islam.

An after-life for people is necessary to maintain justice, which is a deep requirement of life in God's world. During life on Earth there is great injustice. Everyone suffers some injustice, even though for some people it may be only mild. But for many people there is severe injustice, either because of the actions of people selfishly causing harm to others, or because of ill health, injury or misfortune that has blighted their lives while on Earth. To achieve justice, there has to be a place, and mechanisms, where these injustices can be made good. The after-life in the world of the spirit will provide the solace and joy that will wipe away the tears of the sufferers. They will have justice, not dependent on punishment of those who have wronged them, but through being free of suffering and living in the warmth of God's love. Those people who have turned their back on God during their life on Earth may be cut off from this, to their eternal remorse.

It is not possible to imagine what this spiritual world is like. It is often referred to as a non-material world because it cannot be detected by the physical methods of science. But it must have some structure and laws of its own; it is not "nothing". It is something that at present we cannot see but is none the less real. I prefer to think of it as an "other-material" world made of spiritual stuff that we do not, and as yet cannot, understand. It must be separate to the physical world, but closely intertwined with the physical world, because there are interactions between the two. It could be imagined to be in relationship with the physical world in the same way as the strands of thread in a woven cloth; the warp and the weft, which are closely intertwined together. God is not of the physical world but observes it and is in contact with the physical world.

The first of the evidences for the existence of the spiritual world must be the almost universal belief that people have in God. Atheists may seem quite numerous in parts of Western countries, but they are numerically a very small proportion of the seven billion people now living. People believe in God because when they pray they know that God is listening to them. A person's belief usually begins through parental influence, strengthened by religious institutions, school and friends. But it is the communication with God in prayer that makes belief in God inescapable, something that those who turn their back on God cannot understand because it is something that they have never experienced.

There is only one God. God is the supreme spiritual being. When one really thinks of a being so powerful, that has always existed and always will exist, the mind cannot encompass such a vast idea. God is so far removed from our ordinary understanding, yet he has made himself known to generations of people, through the prophets and through the speaking and writing of thousands of people down the ages. The greatest of the prophets are known as the Great Universal Prophets: Abraham, Noah, Moses, Jesus and Muhammad.

The spiritual world is thought to include Satan, the fallen angel who rebelled against God and was driven out of Heaven by the archangel Gabriel. He personifies evil in all its forms. But evil comes from the selfishness that people cannot overcome in their dealings with other people and in their own self-indulgence and their own lack of self-discipline. Selfishness is a deep-seated animal instinct that we have all inherited from our animal ancestors and which requires the love of God to moderate. For animals, it is necessary to be selfish: they have to do all they can to survive in a hostile and competitive environment. So to some extent do people, but because of our higher nature, made in the likeness of God, and given a conscience to direct our actions, we are required to do better than animals and to show love and compassion, to help the afflicted and to put other people's needs before our own.

The message of Jesus Christ is the pre-eminence of unselfishness. "A man can give no greater gift than to lay down his life for his friends." And again, "Love God with all your soul and all your heart and all your mind and all your strength and love your neighbour as much as you love yourself." Judaism and Islam also stress the importance of unselfishness.

There are thought to be numerous evil spirits, who are the souls of people who have been guilty of serious wrongdoing. Many people have experience of these evil spirits. The Bible refers to them in several places, especially in the Gospels, where Jesus is reported to have "cleansed people of devils". This is described in detail by Peter Horobin in his scholarly book "Healing by Deliverance". (See Chapter 1).

People have long been fascinated by tales about supernatural events: ghost stories, such as the famous Ingoldsby Legends. These are based on real events. People are affected by evil spirits. Of course, people who have no experience of supernatural events tend to scoff at these stories and say that the people concerned are deluded or fraudulent. But when someone has close personal experience of evil spirits it has a profound effect on them and their view changes very rapidly.

My personal experiences have been deliberately left out for most of this book, but here I would like to share with you some things that have happened to me, over the past twenty years or so, which point to the existence of the spiritual world. These are true experiences, still vividly remembered, which leave me in no doubt about the reality of the spiritual world. But it must be emphasised that my belief in God is not dependent on these things: I believe in God because I pray to God and I know that I am being listened to; just one of seven thousand million people listened to by God at this time.

These personal experiences which support the existence of a spiritual world can be considered under the following headings:

Evil spirits

A good friend of mine suffered from some ill health and was helped by a healer, but she introduced him to the use of a pendulum to try to diagnose his medical condition. As he was by nature a gambler he then started to use the pendulum to seek the results of football matches. Soon after this he began to hear voices of evil spirits, talking to him about his betting. He told me a lot about this because he was very upset by the voices. This led to my first experience of evil spirits. One night I was going to bed, and just after getting into bed and lying down to prepare to sleep, the thought came into my head about my friend and his evil spirits. I thought to myself "I cannot really believe that he is affected by evil spirits." As soon as I had thought that, there was a loud bang-bang by the side of my head, caused by the head-board of the bed being violently pulled back and struck against the wall, two times. I jumped out of bed in great fear, and immediately switched on the light. I felt that there was an evil presence in the room and I was too frightened to go back to sleep for some time, and kept the light on all night long. The fact was that the headboard had been physically moved by something, quite strongly. There was no scientific explanation for this because it happened when I was alone and lying completely still. It was a double bang, a bit like the sonic boom from an aircraft breaking the sound barrier, which I learnt later was characteristic of the noise made by evil spirits.

Another supernatural thing happened one day when I was driving my car past the house where my friend lived. This lay in a small estate with an entrance road to my left. As I passed the entrance road I thought to myself "Can my friend really be affected by evil spirits?" Immediately the car engine stopped running. I was very surprised and coasted to a stop. I then put my hand on the ignition key and found that it was in the "off" position. As soon as I turned it on again, the engine restarted. There is no scientific way to explain how the ignition key came to be turned off as we passed the house.

My friend was so worried about the evil spirits that he asked his priest to come to the house to drive them away. I was with him when the priest came, and we went into the lounge. The priest began to spread Holy Water around the room from a vial in his hand. As soon as he did that, there was a loud "bang-bang" on the patio window. My friend and I both heard it but the priest seemed not to notice. It seemed to us that something was trying to get away from the Holy Water.

None of these three events have any physical explanation; they were physical events caused by a non-physical force. Subsequently my friend has experienced several more similar events. It is, of course, very frightening to think that there are evil spirits around us, who can read our thoughts and can affect both our minds and our bodies. Perhaps that is why many people prefer not to think about such things and hope that they do not exist. But it is better to be aware of these things and to be alert to their presence. It seems possible that some people suffer mental problems that come from the actions of evil spirits, but they do not know that it is evil spirits that are causing their distress.

Psychic surgeon

This same friend developed liver problems due to heavy drinking of alcohol. He developed jaundice and gastrointestinal signs. His doctor arranged for liver function tests to be carried out. They gave very bad results and his doctor said that there had to be a dramatic reduction in drinking, but he carried on drinking as usual. I then took him to be seen by a very well-known and respected Psychic Surgeon: Stephen Turoff.

What happened there was most remarkable. My friend was lying on his back on a bed with his abdomen uncovered. The psychic surgeon was standing next to the head of the bed and I was standing at the foot of the bed, watching. Stephen began pressing his hands on the lower right side of the abdomen (about where the incision is made for an appendectomy) I was amazed to see an intense black staining of the skin, underneath his hands, forming an area about six inches (15 cms) across. After a few seconds, Stephen noticed that I had seen this, and covered the stain as much as he could with his hands so that I could not see it so well. He continued pressing for another minute or two, then removed his hands. The stain had completely gone. I have thought a lot about this and I can think of no way to explain how such an intense dark stain could come and then go again in such a short time. Some days after that the jaundice disappeared and the black tarry stools returned to normal. About three weeks later another blood test was done. Although still drinking as much alcohol as ever, the liver function test results were now back in the normal range. Amazing though this is, it seemed that the surgeon must have removed some damaged liver which was replaced with new liver. There had been symptoms of liver cirrhosis, which is usually incurable, but it got better. Apart from that, what impressed me most was the physical staining of the skin, like black ink, which appeared so quickly but then disappeared after about one minute. Surely a manifestation of the non-material world affecting our physical world in a way we cannot understand.

A few years later, I myself experienced the healing power of God, through Stephen Turoff. I had been suffering unpleasant back-pain for about a year, following a minor road traffic accident. I had followed the usual course of being seen by a doctor, an orthopaedic surgeon, a physiotherapist, a chiropractor and an osteopath. None of them had provided me with any relief. I lay on by stomach and I felt severe pain as Stephen make cuts across my spine (although he had only his bare hands). The pain ended almost immediately and after a couple of minutes I got off the bed. The friend who had taken me there looked at my back and could see pink marks on my skin, which she photographed and showed me later. It looked just like a long surgical wound over my spine, which had healed, even having small spots on either side where sutures had been. My back felt very stiff, as though it had been fused together, and remained like that for about three days, but then relaxed again. All the pain had gone from my back and from that time on I have had no pain in my back.

About two years later I visited Stephen again because I became worried about my blood pressure, which showed a normal range systolic pressure but a diastolic pressure a lot too low, which is a bad thing to have. I lay on my back and Stephen pressed on my chest, just above the sternum. It was intensely painful for about 10 seconds and I had difficulty not to cry out in pain. The pain disappeared and after a few minutes of gentle pressure I was able to get up and leave. For about two weeks after this I felt weak and tired, as though I was suffering from the after effects of heart surgery. After another month, my blood pressure gave good readings for both systolic and diastolic values. Now, two years later, my blood pressure is 120/60 which is remarkably good for an older man.

I am convinced that God works through Stephen to carry out wonderful healing.

Telepathy

There seems to be some truth in the idea of telepathy. There have now been several times when I suddenly decided to send a text message (SMS) to a close woman friend and after writing a few words and before sending the text message I received a telephone call from her. It has not happened with anyone else and probably depends on a close friendship developing over many years. This kind of thing is quite often reported by all sorts of people and does suggest that there is some way in which our thoughts can be transmitted over long distances.

Water divining

Some years ago, around 2005, I visited a dear friend of many years who owned a small farm in Dorset. He had invited me to join him for lunch and meet another old friend, from his school days, whom I had not met before. We spent a very pleasant few hours together. During this time my friend told us how an old man who was a water diviner had been talking to him the previous year. The man had shown my friend how to select a suitable branch from a willow tree and how to cut it to shape, then leave it to dry out for six months. The bark is left on. The branch has to have a Y shape, with two long arms (about a foot long) and a short base about three inches long. It is fairly slim, about three quarters of an inch in diameter.

My friend told us that he had done all this, and had recently decided the stick had dried for long enough, so he had tried using it. He had been surprised by what happened because, being a scientist, he had expected very little or nothing to happen. He took us to a grassy path by the farm and invited me to hold the stick and walk along the path. I held one of the long arms in each hand, thumbs pointing forwards, and with the point facing forwards, keeping the whole thing parallel to the ground.

As I walked along the path I was amazed when the stick started twisting in my hands, so that the point began to turn down towards the ground. I found that the stick was twisting in such a way that the two long arms were turning on their long axis, in an outward direction (clockwise on the right, anti-clockwise on the left) which resulted in the point dipping down. I tried to stop the turning but however hard I made my grip I could not stop the twisting. As I walked on, the stick began turning back the opposite way, and once again I could not stop the movement, the turning was so strong that I could not arrest it. My friend told me that there was a water pipe crossing the path, about two feet below the surface, and that must be what was causing the willow wand to twist. But how could it do that? What amazed me was the power in the stick, not just a gentle twitch but a turning so strong that I could not stop it however hard I gripped the wood with both hands. The rough bark was scratching the palms of my hands as it kept twisting.

Our other friend also tried it and experienced exactly the same as I had done. We were all very impressed and mystified by what had happened. It made a very strong impact on me, taking place before the other spiritual events mentioned above. It made me think that there must be another world which is in contact with ours but which operates with different mechanisms and forces.

Of course water divining has been subject to scientific study. Water diviners have been asked to search for water in arid districts, and their results have been analysed and often found to be about 50/50, so could have been due to chance.

That is not the point here. The point that struck me so strongly was that where there was some water nearby, how was that water able to cause such a strong movement in the stick. It could not be explained in terms of humidity or dryness or any such things. The movement was so strong and so immediate. It would be difficult to twist dry wood like that, if one applied clamps to the wood and twisted them, the force required would be great. I remember so clearly how it felt, and I have not heard any scientific explanation for what I experienced. It is strong evidence for a non-material world affecting our material world, or else for some other physical mechanism in our world that is as yet unknown to science.

Language

The last point I would like to make here is that the language we all speak is a spiritual thing. It is not material. It has no mass or dimension or position in space. It is purely a set of ideas that exist in the minds of people. Of course words that are spoken have a physical basis—sound waves, and written words have a physical basis—the paper or papyrus, ink, stone, clay or screen used to form the words, but the words themselves, the meaning of the words themselves, have no material structure, they are completely of the spiritual world. In fact that applies to all our thoughts: thinking is a purely spiritual activity. The brain plays a part in the production of thought, but the ideas in the thought are non-material.

Sometimes people ask "Which came first, the physical world or the spiritual world?" In the beginning there was only God. As St John said at the start of his Gospel "In the beginning was the Word, and the Word was with God, and the Word was God." This is such a profound statement. The first thing to exist was the Word, that is to say the carrier of "ideas" and "information". This first produced the spiritual world and the material world came later.

Belief in a spiritual, non-material world is an essential part of belief in God and belief in the existence and reality of an immortal soul.

Some people resolutely refuse to believe in a non-material world of the spirit, and this is frequently a cause of their inability to believe in God. It is unlikely that people who think like that will be much influenced by the personal experiences that I recounted above. Other people, who do believe in a spiritual non-material world, may be interested in my personal observations, which may be similar to some of their own experiences.

7. The Soul and Mind

The idea that a person has an immortal soul which lives on forever after a person's body has died is of pivotal importance because so much else depends upon the concept of life after death. It is the soul that makes the person. Without the soul a person would still be an animal without a conscience and with an existence limited by the longevity of their body. The concept of justice would no longer be part of our world because the inescapable injustices of our physical existence would not be rectified in an after-life.

Earlier in this book it was shown that Natural Selection could not have given people our superabundant intelligence because Natural Selection is a response to a need and it is evident that we have much more intelligence than is needed for a hunter-gatherer. What about the soul? Could Natural Selection have given a person a soul? Certainly not. It could not do so because a soul is a spiritual entity, but Natural Selection is a physical process dependent on physical selection of physical traits as encoded in the genome (plus possible epigenetic inheritance). Only God could have given us our soul.

It seems that a soul is something that a person has which is complete and whole. It is not generally thought that there are different sizes or types of soul. It is generally thought that all souls are of the same nature but specific to an individual. (But see "Jewish religion" below.) The content of the soul defines the individual. So it seems that the soul did not develop by small incremental steps. It was not present in early hominids or indeed in early *Homo sapiens.* The soul appeared suddenly when God "made man in His image".

The idea of a spiritual dimension to people has been present in thinkers' minds for thousands of years. Over these years many people have contributed their views about what the soul is and how it functions. There is a vast literature and it is not within the scope of this book to discuss the soul in any detail. There are also miles of print devoted to the mind. What is the mind, how does it work and how does it relate to the brain and to the soul? The mind enables us to have thoughts and feelings. It gives us the power to reason, to have memory and imagination. It gives us our consciousness and our unconscious cognitive functions.

The brain produces electrical impulses, some of which are associated with thought. Thinking produces electrical impulses which can cause the body to do some things, such as reaching up to pick an apple off a tree or writing about picking apples. So the brain is closely connected to thought but the thoughts themselves are non-material. They have no mass, dimension or position. So our thoughts are spiritual, and part of the spiritual world, even though they are generated by our brains. Brain electrical activity can be detected by an electroencephalogram, but not the thoughts that are associated with the brain signals. Perhaps an analogy would be a radio transmitter. It emits a carrier wave which has oscillations upon it which carry the message. The waves can be detected, but that does not show the words that give meaning to the message.

It is clear that thoughts—mental activity—the mind of people, are associated with the brain but it is not clear how this works or what else is required to make it work. A thought cannot be seen or heard or smelled or touched. It cannot be read by any instrument. It exists in the mind, but has no physical property that can be demonstrated scientifically. Despite this, a thought can produce a physical effect. As we have seen, the thought that a person wants to write a certain word causes activity in Purkinje cells which results in the muscular activity needed to form the appropriate letters. Brain waves seen on electroencephalograms, or areas of brain activity seen in fMRI images, show that mental processes are taking place, but do not show what the thoughts are. It is rather like observing that a television receiver is working, but not being able to see or hear the broadcast. This is the trouble with much of the research in neuroscience. It is like dissecting a television set to find out how it works, but gaining no insight into the broadcast programmes it can receive, or how these programmes came to be made and transmitted.

Thus thoughts must be seen as supernatural events. As we all think thoughts, it is odd that some people deny the supernatural. What the oft quoted Rene Descartes should have said was not "I think, therefore I exist" but "I think, therefore I am *supernatural.*"

But is thought more than the brain? The answer to this depends on whether it is given by someone who thinks there is nothing but the physical world or someone who thinks there is a non-material world. To the latter it appears that the mind is more than the brain and that the mind is closely joined to the soul.

My belief is that the brain, mind and soul are closely connected. It is an imperfect analogy, but the brain can be likened to the hardware of a computer. The mind can be likened to the software in a computer. The soul can be likened to the keyboard operator.

The soul is not a bit of something floating around outside oneself and loosely attached. The soul is embedded deeply inside oneself, the real absolute you, the thinking person that you are. Thought begins with the soul. It is the soul that generates thought, it is there in the soul were thought begins. The soul uses language, the word, to make thoughts. The thoughts of the soul are collected and saved into the mind, which can arrange the thoughts and thus facilitate learning and memory. The mind is able to cause the brain to activate muscles which will produce speech or writing to make these thoughts manifest to others. When a person dies, it is not the end of their thinking. Their soul continues to think as before but the mind is not able to activate the brain to make speech or writing, because the brain is dead, and therefore the thoughts of the soul can no longer be made manifest.

In the early Christian centuries, it was thought that people consisted of a body and a soul and a spirit. But later scholars said that in the Bible "soul" and "spirit" were often used interchangeably and could not be distinguished from one another. It was decided at the Council of Constantinople in AD 869 that the idea of three components was not correct. It was said that a person consists of two components: a body and a soul. But it may be that one *should* think of three components: body (brain), mind and soul. Jesus of Nazareth gave us the two Great Commandments. In the first commandment he said "You shall love the Lord your God with all your heart and with all your soul and with all your mind and with all your strength." In this, he indicated that the soul and mind were distinct from each other. The heart is often thought of as the seat of the emotions—a loving heart, a heartfelt plea, or a heartless person—and the heart does seem to respond to emotional feelings.

[Comment on the two Great Commandments, which are linked together:

"You shall love the Lord your God with all your heart and with all your soul and with all your mind and with all your strength."

The second is like to it, "You shall love your neighbour as much as you love yourself."

It is easy to love God, because God is wonderful and perfect in every way; full of power and love and mercy. But loving our neighbour is difficult because many of our neighbours are disagreeable and many may cause us harm. But how do we show our love for God? The way to show our love for God is to show love to our neighbours. That is the way we have to do it, hard though it may be. That is the Will of God.]

The ancient Egyptians believed in a spiritual part of the person which survived death. Aristotle, Plato, Socrates and other ancient writers had their own ideas about the soul and there is much variation in the way that more recent people have thought about the soul.

The main variables in thinking about the soul are:

Is the soul partly a life-force which keeps the body alive?

Is the soul immortal?

Does the soul die when the person dies, or go to sleep till the judgement day, or remain fully active from then on, forever?

Does the soul of believers in God last forever but the soul of those who reject God perish?

Does the soul of a person exist before they are born?

How does the soul begin?

Do animals have a soul?

Perhaps the first thing to say is that almost all people, over the ages, have believed that people do have a spiritual being that is distinct from their body. Various names have been given to this with wider or narrower meaning. Let us just call it the soul.

I think that the idea that the soul is a life-force keeping the physical body alive is no longer widely held except partly in the Jewish religion—see below. Science can explain that cells remain alive until killed by lack of oxygen or nutrients, extreme heat or cold, or toxic molecules. Life can only be created from pre-existing life, it is never formed *de novo* nowadays, as far as we know. But maybe there is something else as well? We do not know.

I think that the most prevalent idea is that the soul is immortal. The logical steps in this belief are that God is everlasting and that God made man in his image and likeness, meaning that God gave people immortality. This is of course confirmed by the death of Jesus Christ on the Cross and the fact that he was seen alive again by many witnesses. There is no doubt that Jesus was dead when his body was given to Joseph of Arimathea because the Roman soldiers would have known the signs of death and would not have dared risk giving away a still living body, for fear of their own execution. The resurrection of Jesus Christ shows that life after death is possible. But the soul is a spiritual being, so it does not die and get resurrected (as the body of Jesus did); it simply goes on as before, but independently from the body. As stated above and elsewhere in this book our immortality is necessary to maintain justice. Many good people suffer in this life and there needs to be some comfort for them.

There are many different ideas about what happens to the soul when a person dies. There is a widespread belief amongst Christians that when a person dies they go to Heaven (or Hell). But the orthodox Christian teaching is that there will be a Judgement Day, sometime next week or next century or next millennium or later when all the dead will be judged by Jesus Christ. This would mean that the souls of the dead are "sleeping" until the Day of Judgement. After that, the soul would go to Heaven or Hell, or to Purgatory to be purged of sin.

It may be that when an unbeliever dies their soul will also die: an act of mercy so that their soul does not suffer everlasting torment because of being separated from the love of the God they denied. (Rather like Voltaire's Pangloss being grateful to be hanged, rather than being burnt at the stake.)

All these ideas are possibilities and there is no way of knowing for certain which are right or wrong, because of our inability to observe or conduct experiments with spiritual things. The more one thinks about these ideas the more amazing and unknowable they become. Have faith in the love of God and in his power and mercy.

Some people think that the soul exists before a person is born. But where would it be and how does it get to the baby at the appropriate time? There is speculation about when the soul begins: is it at the time of conception, the time of birth, or somewhere between?

My own belief is that the soul begins to develop as the embryo develops. It will begin as a very rudimentary soul when the brain stem is laid down and will gradually develop synchronously with the development of the brain and mind, to be complete by the time of birth. I envisage the soul continuing throughout life, being the guiding force and essence of the person, the expression of their personality. It is a bit like a recording of the person's life, which is made as it happens. I think of it being like a woven tapestry illustrating and recording their life, which unrolls as a carpet might emerge from the loom on which it is being woven, getting longer and longer with each throw of the bobbin. When the person dies, the soul continues thinking and remains as a long string that is their everlasting being. It is a record of every second of their life. It is "read only"— it cannot be changed. But any part of it can be examined at will—perfect recall. This is the soul that God will judge. It may then either live joyfully in the light and warmth of God's love or be shut off from God's love, to shiver in remorse, until, perhaps, forgiven.

Some people believe in reincarnation: that when a person dies their soul enters the body of a new infant (or lower animal) and lives another life, a process that can be repeated many times. I find that difficult to accept because it is too complicated. But if it is true it would simply delay the final stage by some generations.

The ancient writers tended to believe that animals have souls, and even that trees and rivers had souls. But that is rarely believed today. If animals had souls, at what point in development would this happen—spiders, frogs, chickens? Or only mammals. But the fact is that God said "Let us make man in our image and in our likeness we will make him." Which means that only people have souls within the meaning that we are thinking about here. Perhaps the higher animals have something else, which is similar to a soul?

God gave the first persons their souls, there is no other possible explanation. Subsequently, it is a question whether God creates each soul as a baby develops, or whether the soul of the baby develops spontaneously because the original creation of people set up the correct conditions in the foetus for a soul to develop. The latter view would sit more comfortably with the present view that God set up the conditions for creation and acted at some critical control points, but does not have to be active every day in maintaining creation.

In the Jewish religion, a more complex idea of the soul has developed over many centuries. As I understand it, Jewish people believe that the soul consists of three parts which are named Nefresh, Ruachand and Neshama. Nefresh is closely concerned with the body and life-force. Neshama is the highest of the three levels of the soul and closest to God, concerned mainly with the spiritual life. Ruach is between these two; it connects man to his spiritual source. The Neshama is affected only by thought, the Ruach by speech and the Nefresh by action. The concept of the soul and immortality are fundamental to the Jewish religion but there is little detail about what the afterlife might be like: no one has heard or seen the world to come, except God. The main emphasis of the religion is to promote and facilitate a good and Godly life in this physical world.

Islam believes in a soul which survives the death of the body. When a person dies, the soul is extracted from the body by the Angel of Death. If the person has led a good life, this will be a fairly pain-free experience. The good soul will be taken to Heaven, briefly, then returned to earth to remain in some comfort, waiting for the Day of Judgement. The soul of a bad person will fear to leave the body and will be torn out of the body, causing great pain. It will then descend to Hell, to be punished there until the Day of Judgement. Other religious traditions have their own beliefs about the soul and the after-life.

It is necessary for all believers in God to be strong in stating that people could not have been made by Natural Selection. Only God, the maker of the spiritual world, could have given us our souls and the super-intelligence and exquisitely complex language that we now have. Why do we have the ability to talk so well? It is to enable us to talk to God. People were made by God so that we could talk to him, worship him, and tell him all our hopes and fears. That is the reason, the only reason, for our existence.

8. Language

Language is wonderful: amazing, incredible, fantastic. We are the only living beings who have language. Why do we have it? How did we get it? Why do none of the other animals or plants have language?

Some people deny how amazing language is. Sometimes people try to make a case that some animals do have language. But these are both mistaken ideas.

The language spoken by people for thousands of years is very complex. It is a syntactical language, based on grammatical rules which give it structure. All people who are not brain damaged are born with the ability to speak a language and they quickly learn the language which they hear around them after birth. They have the ability to learn more than one language at the same time as they grow up, if they hear different languages around them. This is a truly amazing fact of our lives.

It is worse than simplistic for people to study apes and conclude that they have language on the basis of a dozen different grunts. Contrast that with the language of the people who are studying them. The people have language which can describe and analyse their observations. The apes have very simple communication with each other but do not study the language of the observers and are unable to describe anything.

A few grunts do not constitute a language. Language is what *people* speak, the rich and varied language which people use when we talk to God and to each other, the wonderfully expressive, complex and infinitely adaptable language that we read in the works of writers such as Virgil to Voltaire or Socrates to Shakespeare or Dickens to Damon Runyon, and of course the language and literature of other cultures from around the world.

Our language enables us to think elaborately. To build complex intellectual concepts. To think in the abstract about the past and the future. To explain to ourselves and to others our innermost thoughts and feelings. To express our emotions clearly without waving our arms or kicking and punching. Most importantly it enables us to talk to God. Language is necessary for a person to understand the difference between good and evil. Without language it is not possible to construct the ideas that describe these concepts and sin becomes impossible as with the animals. When a person has language, they can think about their life and their possessions, and compare themselves to others. This can lead to defining their wants and frustrations and expressing their envious or violent thoughts. It also gives the ability to express these ideas to another person, who may agree with them and stoke up their anger and determination to take violent action to steal what they want. Use of language can enable one individual to have a strong influence on a number of others. This can be for the good of the group and be perfectly good in its nature, but can also be good for the group in an evil way, if the group leader wants them to do wrong. It is only through the use of language that political leaders can persuade populations to be guided by them and follow their instructions. Language is very important in the formation of relationships between people within their family and the making of new friendships outside the family. It is of great importance in the development of a loving relationship and in maintaining a happy marriage.

Language is not just a minor attribute of people. It is of overwhelming importance. People love talking. Wherever one sees two or more people together, they are almost always talking to each other. They talk to share their experiences, their hopes and fears. They talk to exchange ideas and to influence each other, to impress or attract each other. Myriads of reasons, but always talking, talking. Normally young children babble, and as soon as they can talk, they are especially talkative.

How unique we are. Look out at the sky on a starry night and think of all those billions of stars reaching out to very distant galaxies, and in all that great physical mass there is no thought and no language save for God and us. (And perhaps the Aliens someone will say).

There is no agreement about how long in the past it was that language began. Some scholars think that it might have been present a very long time ago, based on extrapolation backwards of rate of change in a language. Extrapolation is always a very unsafe procedure and especially in a case such as this, where the data are very shaky and the time span is very great. I think such calculations can be safely ignored. It seems to me safe to assume that language was not present one hundred thousand years ago, even though some linguists think that language was present that long ago, or longer. A factor to consider is the time it took for spoken language to become written language. In my opinion, it would not have taken one or two hundred thousand years for that to happen. It is most likely that spoken language appeared about 70,000 years ago at the moment when people were given a soul, and that written language followed a few thousand years after the change to sedentism and agriculture which took place 10,000 years ago. The first evidence we have of writing dates to about 6,500 years ago and that is the first time that we know for certain that there was language.

Certainly there was a time when language was not spoken at all. Now we have this amazing language spoken by everyone. How did this transition from no language to universal language occur?

The quasi-scientific theories which have been thought up over the past two hundred years about the development of language without the involvement of God are most unconvincing.

A very useful summary of early theories of language has been published on the Internet by Arika Okrent and can be found in *mentalfloss.com*. I am indebted to the author for the following information who wrote:

"How did language begin? Words don't leave artefacts behind and writing began long after speech so theories of language origins have generally been based on hunches. For centuries there has been so much fruitless speculation. The early theories have been given short distinguishing names. All are unsupportable."

They are briefly described below:

The bow-wow theory

The idea that speech arose from people imitating the sounds that things make: bow-wow, moo, baa etc.

Not likely, since very few things we talk about have characteristic sounds associated with them, and very few of our words sound anything at all like what they mean.

The pooh-pooh theory

The idea that speech comes from the automatic vocal response to pain, fear, surprise or other emotions. A laugh, shriek, a gasp.

But plenty of animals make these sounds too, and they didn't end up with language.

The ding-dong theory

The idea that speech reflects some mystical resonance or harmony connected with things in the world.

The yo-he-ho theory

The idea that speech started with the rhythmic chants and grunts that people used to coordinate their physical actions when they worked together. There is a pretty big difference between this kind of thing and what we do most of the time with language.

The ta-ta theory

The idea that speech came from the use of tongue and mouth gestures to mimic manual gestures. For example, saying ta-ta is like waving good bye with your tongues. But most of the things we talk about do not have characteristic gestures associated with them, much less gestures you can imitate with your tongue and mouth.

The la-la theory

The idea that speech emerged from the sounds of inspired playfulness, love, poetic sensibility and song. This one is lovely but no more or less likely than the others.

Nowadays scientists consider which physical, cognitive and social factors must first be in place in order for there to be language."

The idea that language could have developed slowly over a long period of time is unsupportable because a very small amount of language is next to useless, as I know to my cost when trying to speak Spanish or French when abroad. Language is only useful and therefore worth learning once enough has been learnt to communicate ideas effectively with another person. It takes quite a time to reach this level. A child learns the basics of a language quickly and uses grammar and syntax at an early age. At only about one year of age, a child has understanding of causative sentences, such as "the boy pushed the chair". Over the past 70 years there has been a lot of thought given to trying to understand how it is that a child acquires the ability to speak. The first notable work on this subject is regarded to be that of an American psychologist, B.F. Skinner. He published a book called Verbal Behaviour in 1957. He proposed that children learn language through association of a sound with an object or action. If a mother gives her child an apple and says "Apple" the child will remember the association between that word and object. This seems perfectly reasonable and must account for the very first learnt words. But the concept was later criticised by Noam Chomsky who wrote extensively on this subject and is highly regarded as a linguist. He thought that the rather simplistic explanation of Skinner was not sufficient to explain the way in which a child can learn to create complex sentences at an early age. That requires the ability to break down the sentences that the child hears into meaningful segments, which can be rearranged and strung together in many different ways to express new ideas. It is amazing that this can be done, considering the speed with which adults talk, leaving little space between words, but somehow a child can separate the words correctly. Putting the words together in the right order requires a knowledge of grammar: putting words into categories such as nouns or verbs. Chomsky proposed that the mind of every child contains a Language Acquisition Device (LAD) which encodes the major principles of language and its grammatical structures into the child's brain: it is a set of rules that enable the child to construct meaningful sentences (although as Chomsky pointed out, a sentence can be grammatically correct but meaningless, giving as an example "colourless green ideas sleep furiously"). It is noteworthy that medieval scholars also thought that grammar was something that was there, already made by God, not something invented by people. It seems to me that there is a certain inevitability about grammar. It has to be that way, to work. There are bound to be words that are the name of things (nouns) and other words that are the name of actions (verbs). All languages work that way. With the LAD in the child's brain, they only have to learn new vocabulary and apply the syntactic structures from the LAD to form correct sentences. But sometimes a young child will be heard saying, for example "readed". They do not yet know the irregular form of the past tense (and they have certainly never heard anyone say "readed") but somehow they have sensed that adding "ed" to a verb makes it a past action.

Nowadays, when a young child hears language and tries to copy it, they will be heard by people who know the language which is long existing, and they will encourage the child's efforts by their responses to the child's words: there will be encouragement and reinforcement. That is very different to an ancient hominid having a genetic mutation which gave them some language ability, because it would only be present in them, and perhaps a few siblings, but nobody else would understand what they were saying. There would be no reinforcement or encouragement.

A child learns language by hearing it spoken by others. This is a continual regress until the first people to speak, who had no person to learn from. Therefore they must have been taught to speak by God.

Despite all the work and thought that has gone into this, there is still very little understanding of how children acquire language. It seems to me that the study of the development of the ability to speak a language, in children, has little or no relevance to the way in which language might have developed in the first place. It is rather like studying the way in which people learn how to drive a motor car. This throws no light on how cars came to be first invented. Children are alive now and can be questioned and examined with brain scans, but little is really understood about the mechanism of language acquisition. How much more difficult it is to understand how language developed initially.

So I think that Skinner and Chomsky were both correct, but in later decades Noam Chomsky's work has been criticised by people who do not like the idea of a set of rules given instantly at some time in the past: they are fixed on the idea of Natural Selection however unrealistic that may be in this particular context.

Since Chomsky published his ideas about the acquisition of language in children there has been further development of theories about the way in which language developed in prehistory. Recent theories can be divided into two categories, known as "Continuity theories" and "Discontinuity theories". The former are based on the idea that language must have developed slowly over a long period of time, in much the same way that other characteristics may have evolved in small steps over time. The latter is the opposite; that language must have appeared quite suddenly. It is said that a majority of people who study linguistics at the present time hold to some form of continuity theory, no doubt much too influenced by Natural Selection. Some see language as a mainly innate quality which evolved gradually. Others see it as mainly cultural.

There has evidently been a great amount of thought given to this subject in recent years with an extensive published literature which I will not attempt to review here. Modern theories are not much different from the older ones described above. They tend to be based on either the use of gestures leading on to language or meaningless sounds acquiring meaning over time. There are supporting arguments and counter-arguments for them all, with no agreed conclusion at the present time.

Much of the modern thinking on this subject is concerned with observation and interpretation of primate gestures and sounds. It seems to me that such observations have no relevance to the way in which language appeared in people, for two reasons:

1. The primates have existed for a very long time in their present form. For example, there are two species of gorilla: *Gorilla beringei* and *Gorilla gorilla*, each with two sub-species. Both diverged about two million years ago and were separated by the River Congo. Over all this long time their gestures and sounds did not develop into any language.
2. Even if the appearance of language in humans is set 200,000 years ago, by that time the human line had developed through several species away from the primates. The humans of that time were very far removed from apes with regard to behaviour and intellect. They were humans, not animals, and therefore animal studies are irrelevant.

The trouble with all the modern theories is that they are predicated upon the idea of Natural Selection, which does not apply in this situation, because there was no special need for language created by environmental change. Natural Selection concerns physical properties of the material world but language is a non-material mental activity. It is therefore legitimate to seek explanations for the appearance of language in the world of the spirit rather than force it into some kind of neo-Darwinian materialist/determinist model. No other living thing has developed language.

I think that Chomsky was correct to suppose that language developed in one great leap, not by slow, small steps. But his idea that it was due to a mutation in one gene seems unlikely because language is such a complex thing, which depends on several separate mental and physical attributes. If it was genetic, it would therefore require several genes to be involved in coordinated changes at the same time. Such a genetic change has not happened within the time span we are considering here: we are genetically the same as sixty or seventy thousand years ago.

It is instructive to try to imagine a small group of hunter-gatherers, some long time ago, and try to think how they might have begun to talk. It seems to me that if one of them had started to make special sounds, perhaps pointing to objects and uttering different sounds, they would have been ignored by the others. After a time, if they persisted, the others in the group might begin to think that there was something wrong with this man or woman. It is very unlikely that they would take an interest and begin to copy the sounds and learn the associated objects. More likely they would ostracise the individual, or attack them. As there would be no immediate advantage in the use of language in those circumstances it would not have been selected for.

Language could only have started with a sudden, overnight, new ability given to a group of people living closely together, at the same time. It would have had to be enough language to be instantly usable in the group and there would have to have been enough mutual trust to allow it to be accepted and used. It would then begin to give some advantages. I discussed this once with an old friend who was a professor of physiology. He told me that he thought the first advantage of language would have been in helping to choose a mate. That was a very sound observation, because language is important in courtship.

As far as I can tell there is nothing science can offer on this subject. The origin of language is really outside the reach of scientific enquiry because of the lack of observable and measurable quantities. We do not have the information to make realistic assumptions. People may try to dress up their ideas as being scientific but in reality they are just speculative guesswork.

It is the first beginnings of language that cannot be explained. Once there was a reasonably workable language in place, it is easy to see how it would grow in complexity and reach as time went by. But I believe that the initial language ability must have been given as a whole, in one package, at one time. It would not have worked otherwise.

It seems to me that there are four distinct modules that needed to have been in place for the first language to occur. These are:

1. Realisation of the concept of language. This is something that does not exist outside the minds of people who do speak language. Animals such as a cat or dog do not have in their minds the idea that it would be possible to make sounds that could be used to describe actions or things. This is the first fundamental step, and it represents a huge jump in understanding.

2. Knowledge of the rules of grammar and syntax, as postulated by Noam Chomsky.

3. A first, simple vocabulary of words that could be used to express simple ideas, such as "I am thirsty" or "Are you thirsty?"
4. A high degree of mutual trust within the community which began to talk, because it is very easy to falsify words and to deliberately use words to mislead people. This is one of the important difficulties about language development that are recognised by scholars: words are "cheap", that is, they are easily given different meanings, so a high level of mutual trust between speakers is necessary.

All four of these components would need to have been present in the minds of the original language speakers, at the same time. It would have to have been a basic bundle of information given to people at one time. It would have given them the power of instant speech in their community. Simple but effective speech, which would increase in power when more words were added to their vocabulary.

Only God could have put all these modules together. It would have had to work, instantly, or it would have been disregarded and unused. This fits with the Genesis description of God talking with Adam and Eve. There is no suggestion of a period of learning, it was something that they could do, a part of their being. God gave people our immortal soul and at the same time the ability to speak language. The two things are inseparably linked. The difference between inanimate nature and God is the Word. In the first verse of the Gospel of Saint John, he wrote "In the beginning was the Word, and the Word was with God, and the Word was God." This shows such deep insight that it must have come direct from God. It is the Word that is reason and cognition. Words are the basic building blocks on which thought depends: without words constructive thought is impossible. We use words to formulate ideas and without words the ideas cannot be constructed. Words also give us a much higher level of consciousness than can be present in an animal without language. Without words there can be only vague, undefined feelings, but with words the feeling can be expressed with great clarity and precision. Even such a simple thing as feeling cold will usually be accompanied by the person thinking or saying to themselves "I feel cold." The very first that existed must have been the Words that enable rational thought and were God. The development of the physical world depended on this.

Of course spoken words depend on a mechanism that can cause vibrations in the air and an ear and a brain that can hear and understand. The first words must have been spiritual entities: words in the mind of God.

So God gave to us people not only the spiritual being of the Soul, but also the language and cognitive ability of the Word. These two together make us what we are.

No other animal has developed language, although they have had just as long as we have had to do so. The ancient hunter-gatherers would have been able to lead their simple lives perfectly well without language, just as the Gorillas have done. There was evidently no need for language in the Darwinian sense of Natural Selection. There must have been some special reason that caused people to have language.

I believe that the reason was to enable us to talk to God. The Creator willed there to be one living creature that could talk to him, to tell him about their lives, their hopes and fears and to worship him. This is an integral part of the Creator's will to have one creature that has an immortal soul. The two things are inseparably linked: language and the soul. Both must have appeared instantly, together, at the same time. It is not known when this happened but in a later chapter it will be suggested that the giving of soul and language most probably happened about 70,000 years ago, just before the migration out of Africa.

The sudden giving of language ability to a group of people might at first seem unlikely, but we know that this did happen at the time of Jesus of Nazareth. The Bible tells us how this happened (Acts. 2. Verses 4 to 11):

"And they were all filled with the Holy Ghost, and began to speak with other tongues, as the Spirit gave them utterance.

"And there were dwelling at Jerusalem Jews, devout men, out of every nation under heaven.

"Now when this was noised abroad, the multitude came together, and were confounded, because that every man heard them speak in his own language.

"And they were all amazed, and marvelled, saying one to another, Behold, are not all these which speak Galileans?

"And how hear we every man in our own tongue, wherein we were born?

"Parthians, and Medes, and Elamites, and the dwellers in Mesopotamia, and in Judea, and Cappadocia, in Pontus and Asia.

"Phrygia, and Pamphylia, in Egypt, and in the parts of Libya about Cyrene, and strangers of Rome, Jews and proselytes.

"Cretes and Arabians we do hear them speak in our tongues the wonderful works of God."

The idea that language was given to people because God wanted people to be able to talk to him would be disputed by people who do not believe in God. But such people have to provide some plausible alternative way to explain *why* we have language and how we first *acquired* language. At present, science cannot provide answers to either of these questions. This seems to be accepted by everyone who is studying the origin of language. A scientific explanation may be forthcoming eventually and if that happens we will understand the *acquisition* mechanism involved, but that will still leave the reason *why* we can speak language undeclared by science. The idea that it was God's will is a logical and reasonable proposition.

Most people use language at every opportunity to express their wishes, feelings and ideas. While recognising the supreme importance of language as something that distinguishes between people and animals, it must be acknowledged that a person who is without language is still a person and has all the other attributes which prove the difference from animals.

It is sad that some people cannot talk, because they miss so much through not having language. Some people have the misfortune to be "deaf and mute" from birth, sometimes as a result of their mother having rubella infection while pregnant. I have known one such person, a very fine man who overcame his handicap wonderfully. He learnt sign-language and he taught himself to become a skilled carpenter and plumber. People like him have all the other attributes that make a person a person, and are no less a person through lack of language although they have a severe handicap to overcome. But it remains true that being talkative is the most obvious quality that is seen in people but in no other life.

In the final chapter, the idea will be advanced that people were given a soul and language instantly and completely just before the migration out of Africa about 70,000 years ago, at the time when there were thought to be only a small number of humans living. This was followed by 60,000 years of simple nomadic life during which time the people remained innocent and peaceable. During this 60,000 years the language spoken would have been the same as we have now in its structure, but would have been restricted to few words because the lives of the people were very simple, so that they would not have needed to name many things or describe many actions. About 10,000 years ago there was a sudden increase in the complexity of life associated with sedentism and agriculture, which would have led to a rapid increase in vocabulary as people did more things and had more possessions. People were also living in much larger social groups and this would also have stimulated the further development of language. It was at that time that inequality between individuals began to develop, leading to the appearance of latent evil in the form of envy and violence which were the driving forces for the change from hunter-gatherers to village dwellers. The increasing expressiveness of the language would have been beneficial and good, but would probably have also contributed to increasing violence and theft.

This proposition will be discussed further in the final chapter of this book. It is not science, it is theology, but it is theology that fits the science of the material record as revealed by archaeology, and fits the words in the Bible.

9. The Bible Regarding Creation

Why is there something rather than nothing? That is a fundamental question. It is answered by those who believe in God by saying that first there was only God, but God wanted something to love, so he created something to love. For someone who does not believe in God there is no answer, except to say "It just happened" which is not satisfying emotionally or intellectually.

There have been many different ideas about how the world was created. This has interested people for thousands of years. Some of the very old ideas seem really strange to us now, such as the idea that the world was supported on the back of a giant turtle. This idea probably started in ancient Hindu mythology but it is also found in ancient Chinese writing. A similar idea was believed by North American indigenous peoples many years ago.

The Judeo-Christian faiths base their belief in creation on the first book of the Bible: Genesis. There is some disagreement about how Genesis came to be written. It may have been written as a single narrative, but with several versions, which were eventually edited into one. Alternatively, there may have been several fragments, dealing with different aspects, which were later combined into one book.

Genesis is the first book in the Bible. The first five books are known collectively as the Pentateuch. They describe the creation of the world in the first part of Genesis, followed in the later verses of Genesis by a description of the genealogy of the early generations that followed Adam and Cain. In later chapters, there is a description of the development of the Jewish Nation. Genesis has to be read with this in mind. It establishes the credentials of the Jewish Nation and demonstrates that the God of Abraham, Isaac and Jacob was not just a local God, but was the creator of everything, the supreme and only God who had chosen Israel to be his first people. The Children of Israel were the first people to believe in their being only one God.

There is a great wealth of scholarship devoted to Genesis, with a number of expert commentaries upon it available for study. There are several texts available for scholars to study. The text called the Masoretic text is generally regarded by scholars as the most authentic text to study. This was emphasised by the discovery of the Dead Sea Scrolls, which confirmed much that was written in the Masoretic text. Other important texts are the Samaritan Pentateuch and the Latin Vulgate.

There was a major revision of the Masoretic text about 500 BC. Language, grammar, history and theology were modified, partly to modernise the text and partly to fit in with the secular traditions of the time.

The King James Version of the Bible, used in England for the past four hundred years, was largely based on the translation from Hebrew and Greek by William Tyndale (1494–1536). Some people take each word of this completely literally. But it is unreasonable to give no flexibility over the meaning of a word, considering that the text has undergone so much ancient development and modification, followed by several translations over the centuries before the King James Bible was written in English.

The Bible is the word of God, but it is the word of God as revealed to people and written as best they could. It would have been based on older verbal accounts, passed on from generation to generation by word of mouth. Scholars believe that this verbal transmission of ideas was probably very accurate.

Genesis describes the creation of the world in six days, and on the seventh day God rested. (It is not thought that God needed to rest from exertions in the way that people do. What it signifies is that God had done all he needed to do.) This is perfectly acceptable as a religious statement, although it is not supported by scientific observations. But of course the Bible is not a scientific book. Some very devout Christians refuse to admit that the statement is not literally true. Of course they can think like that if they want to, but it has the unfortunate effect of playing into the hands of some atheists, illustrated by this example. A newspaper reported that a child had been refused membership of the Boy Scouts because he refused to swear allegiance to the Queen and to God. His father proudly said his son "Did not believe in God, and he did not believe the world was made in seven days either."

The celebrated atheist, Richard Dawkins, gets very annoyed by Creationists (in the North American sense) who refuse to accept the geological record regarding the age of the earth and the mutability of species. As there are no reasonable grounds to doubt the Earth being about four billion years old, and life having developed slowly over the past 600 million years, Richard Dawkins is justifiably critical. Such views by Creationists tend to weaken the Christian position and lead to the attitude of the father quoted above. It would be helpful if a slightly more reasonable and flexible approach could be made to the words in Genesis. To support this some considerations are given below.

Genesis describes creation over a number of days, but it does not state that they were Earth days. In fact, they could not have been Earth days, because Genesis states that the light was divided from the dark on the first day, but the sun was not placed in the sky until the fourth day.

Here, and throughout the first three chapters of Genesis, one can see men struggling to make sense of the world they were living in and trying to work out how it had begun. They were inspired by God to do this, but they did not have any scientific knowledge. It is not surprising that there are statements which do not fit exactly with our present-day and very recently acquired scientific knowledge.

In the early Hebrew text, the word used for day was "yom". But the word yom can mean many things depending on context: a day, or other period of time; an epoch.

Science and religion are different. They depend on entirely separate methodologies. As described above, science depends on observation, measurement and calculation but religion depends on revelation, interpretation and faith. So there is no common ground. It is therefore perfectly reasonable to believe the Genesis account of creation as literally true from a religious perspective. The scientific perspective is not relevant to the Bible. It is interesting to learn that the theologian Augustine of Hippo (AD354–430) thought that, for theological reasons, God would have created everything in an instant. He thought the six days too long. But he thought in terms of an instant creation, followed by a long period in which the activity of *ratio* (reason) caused the further development of the world. This aligns very nicely with the Big Bang theory and the subsequent very slow evolution of the cosmos and our Earth. Augustine, who was Bishop of Hippo Regius in North Africa, now Algeria, had a strong influence on the theological thinking of his time and for a long while afterwards. He evidently did not feel restrained in his thinking by the words in Genesis.

The book of Genesis was (re)written about 2,500 years ago. It had to be written in a way that was understandable to people at that time. In those days, people had a very limited idea of how the physical world was constructed. Even 200 years ago, the educated people in England had very little knowledge of the physical world, as can be seen by reading Chambers' *Vestiges.* Therefore it seems likely that the authors of Genesis knew that they had to write a simplified account of creation, much as one would write for a child. Suppose that a young child asked their father "How was our house made?" the father might reply "Well, on the first day men came and dug trenches in the ground and poured in concrete to make foundations. On the second day, they came with bricks to build the walls. On the third day, men came with wood and tiles to make the roof. On the fourth day, men came with pipes and wires to connect water and electricity. On the fifth day, men came with all the things we need in the house and painted and decorated everything. On the sixth day, we were able to come and live in our house. By the seventh day, it was all done." This would be understood by the child and satisfy their needs, even though the time scale was wrong and little detail given. Similarly, the Genesis account is simple, clear and easily understood by anyone.

Even if Genesis had been written with up-to-date knowledge 60 years ago, it would be out of date now because it would not have contained the current Standard Model. But suppose Genesis stated "God created the world with an Initial Singularity followed by a sudden expansion of space time 13.7 billion years ago. It began with the Plank Epoch which lasted from zero to approximately 10^{-43} seconds. The electromagnetic force, strong nuclear force, weak nuclear force and the force of gravity were all present, held together in perfect symmetry." Not many people would understand that even today.

The Bible is the Word of God, but God's word is written down as perceived by man. It is not unreasonable to think that man's perception of the physical world might change with time. Although the theological and moral teaching of the Bible must remain unchanged, views on the physical word could surely be allowed to change as people become more knowledgeable. In his book "Jesus of Nazareth" Joseph Ratzinger draws attention to the two types of law given in the Hebrew legal system: apodictic law and casuistic law, which he said were equivalent to "principles" and "rules". The apodictic law does not change. A frequently given example is the Ten Commandments, which cannot be altered in any way. Casuistic law can be modified under certain circumstances. It usually operates with regard to crime and punishment. A specific wrong act has a specified punishment, but if the wrong act is slightly different or modified by mitigating circumstances, the punishment can be changed to suit the crime. This introduces the concept that change can be permitted where there is a good reason to do so.

Following this concept it might be reasonable to accept that the detail in the creation account given in Genesis is not intended to be unalterable. The main message that the world was created by God cannot be changed, but the details given in Genesis could be altered in line with increased scientific knowledge. That is not to say that the words in Genesis should be changed but that they need not be taken completely literally nowadays, in the light of recent new knowledge.

What is remarkable, in view of the great antiquity of Genesis, is the way that the creation account follows closely, in general form, the way in which science has discovered. It shows a gradual development over time, with life becoming more complex with each step: plants, then fish to birds to mammals and to man. It might have been expected that a primitive society might have placed the creation of man at the beginning, but in Genesis this is correctly placed at the end. There was no need to include a creation account in the Bible at all. But it is there and it fits remarkably well in outline with the scientific knowledge of our age, unknown when Genesis was written. It is therefore unreasonable to quibble over the interpretation of "days" or other dissimilarities.

Scientists have tended to add to confusion by a misconception about the age of the Earth. From a scientific perspective, the Earth is about four billion years old. Humans, in the form of *Homo sapiens*, have existed for perhaps 150,000 years. But it is important to stress that People, like you and me, have only existed for about 70,000 years. So the important thing is to determine what the world was like when it began, for people. What was the world like 70,000 years ago, or more especially about 10,000 years ago, when the hunter-gatherers suddenly changed their way of life to sedentism and agriculture? It was the same then as it is now. The same wild animals and natural plants that we are familiar with now existed then. There has been no perceptible evolution amongst the lions and wolves, rabbits and blackbirds, salmon and frogs, oak trees and ferns, in the last ten millennia. There will have been some small changes, and some new species formed, but the broad picture is unchanged over such a short period of time. There has been virtually no readily perceptible evolution since the world began—for people.

Atheists say that the theory of Natural Selection proposed by Charles Darwin has shown how the living world developed, without the need for a living God to create us. There is a fundamental point which makes such an attitude unreasonable. This is, that the way life developed would look the same, whether it was driven by the environment or by a designer. The theory of Natural Selection is based on the idea that new features of life become established as a result of need. An individual with certain characteristics will prosper more than others of their species, only if their singular characteristic is needed, and therefore gives them a survival advantage. But when a designer develops a new product, what they do is test their prototypes. They test them in the environment for which they are intended to be used. The designer of an aeroplane will use a wind-tunnel, the designer of a submarine will use models in tanks of water. So the environment will guide the designer in modifying the product in just the same way that the environment selects the more fitted individuals. To an outside observer the two methods will appear to be the same.

It is faulty logic to say that because something does not have to be present, it is therefore not present. Logic would say that if something does not have to be present, it may be present or it may not be present. Absence of evidence is not evidence of absence.

All these considerations make it unreasonable to be completely inflexible about a few words. It is the main message that is important. The main message from the first three chapters of Genesis is that God created the world and everything living. God made men and women in his image and likeness. In his image implies that God gave people an immortal soul. God gave people the ability to speak and understand complex language in conversation with him and with each other. They were tempted by Satan and disobeyed God. Then they understood good and evil. God punished man and woman for their disobedience.

What we need to do is to try to see how we can best use Genesis to understand the material world in the light of modern knowledge and in the light it throws on God's will for the living world and especially for people. This will be developed further in later chapters.

When people talk about Creation, they are usually talking about the creation of the material world. But any discussion of reality must include a consideration of the nature and origin of the spiritual world. Of course, some people do not believe that there is a spiritual world. But for most people there is no doubt that the spiritual world is real. God is a spirit. There is a whole world of existence that is not material, in the baryonic sense. We ourselves are spiritual beings, living our material lives for a while in a material, animal body. But our essential nature is to be a living soul, created by God. That is why only God could have created people, only God could have given primitive humans a soul.

Whatever arguments there may be about the creation of the material world, there can be no doubt that the spiritual world was created by and is maintained by God. This is fundamental to most religious doctrines. It is generally thought that the spiritual world existed before the material world, although in Genesis the creation of Heaven was on the second day of creation.

The material world is thought to have had a definite beginning, about 14 billion years ago, and it will end, a very long time in the future. But the spiritual world does not decay; it is not subject to the second law of thermodynamics. It does not run down. It will never end: it is everlasting.

The spiritual world may be thought of as being closely intermeshed with the material world, like the warp and weft of a piece of woven fabric. Thus God is above the material world, and superior to it, but close to it. God is not remote from us: God listens to the thoughts, the words, of seven billion people, but God is not a part of the material world.

No doubt the spiritual world has various laws that govern its operation, just as the material world has, and these must have come from God in the first place. We know nothing about this and can know nothing about it. Science has no tools or methods for detecting the world of the spirit.

One of the great pleasures and satisfactions of life is to be able to thank God for the wonder of the world. The world we live in and we ourselves are so wonderful and it is good to think of this and to glorify the natural world in the spirit of Natural Theology. God is a spirit and created the spiritual world. God created people, by giving primitive humans an immortal soul and the ability to speak very complex language. These are the important things. We owe our existence to God: no amount of Natural Selection, working on primitive humans for however long, could have done that.

10. The Sapient Paradox

I began thinking about the writing of this book around the year 2000. I had the most important ideas that I wanted to write about already mapped out in my mind at that time, although it has taken about twenty years to complete the writing because of the constant interruptions associated with my personal life. But in 2008, I read a book called *Prehistory: the Making of the Modern Mind*, written by Colin Renfrew, now Lord Renfrew of Kaimsthorn the very distinguished Professor of Archaeology at the University of Cambridge. This had a strongly encouraging effect upon me. I had already realised that the development of people from human ancestors was not a steady linear progression in thousands of equally small steps. It had developed that way for millions of years, but was then followed by a great leap forward in recent times. I was delighted to find that this was confirmed with all the authority of Lord Renfrew's book.

The book begins with an explanation of what prehistory is—the history of our world before there were written records that are still available for us to study and that we now know how to read. Lord Renfrew wrote "Since the earliest written records in the world go back no earlier than about 3500 B.C.E., most of the subject matter of prehistory can be approached only through the preliterate material record of the past as revealed to us through archaeology."

The first four chapters of the book describe the development of the discipline of prehistory, and make an excellent introduction to the subject. Much was achieved in the period 1859 to 1940 but soon after that the method of radiocarbon dating was discovered, refined and widely applied, making it possible to fit archaeological material into a universal time frame.

In the second half of the twentieth century there was an impressive development of archaeological theory. Until the 1970s the usual approach had been what is called the cultural-historic method. As a reaction to this, and encouraged by the possibilities of the radiocarbon dating method, a new way of looking at archaeology emerged: the "New Archaeology." This was stimulated to some extent by Carl Popper's insistence that the core of a scientific hypothesis was that it was testable and therefore open to the possibility of being shown to be untrue. The New Archaeology aimed to apply this same kind of rigorous examination and analysis to emerging archaeological statements: an interesting parallel with the emergence of theological science in the same time frame.

Over the past few decades great progress has been made in discovering the prehistory of many countries throughout the world. There is a great wealth of factual information about the past history and culture of many nations. What is still lacking, however, is an overarching understanding of how these separate histories relate to a generalised trend towards the development of more complex societies.

The earliest examples of our own species, *Homo sapiens*, date back more than 150,000 years. The fossil record shows anatomically modern humans in Ethiopia from 150,000 years ago. Recently there have been further finds of fragments of skulls which are structurally very similar, and much older, but it is probably not correct to classify these as *Homo sapiens.*

Archaeologists have tended to think that the advanced qualities that we recognise in humans today date back to the time of the early emergence of *H. sapiens*. Lord Renfrew disputes this, showing that the early *H. sapiens* remained unchanged in their essential behaviour for a very long time before suddenly changing from being hunter-gatherers to sedentary agriculturalists, quite recently. This is what he called the *sapient paradox:* Why did humans remain unchanged for such a long time and what caused the sudden change that happened only about ten thousand years ago?

To quote from Lord Renfrew's book *Prehistory—The making of the modern mind:*

"What accounts for the huge gap from the first appearance of *Homo sapiens* in Europe forty thousand years ago (and earlier in Western Asia) to the earliest agricultural revolution in Western Asia and Europe of ten thousand years ago? This is a time lag of thirty thousand years! If the genetic basis of the new species is different from that of earlier hominids, and of decisive significance, why is that new inherent genetic capacity not more rapidly visible in its effects, in what is seen in the archaeological record? That rather puzzling question may be termed the sapient paradox. It has significant consequences. They become even more obvious if the transition to *Homo sapiens* is set earlier and relocated to Africa. The fossil and the artefactual evidence now converge on siting the human revolution (understood in cultural terms—that is to say, in terms of human behaviour reflected in the surviving material culture) in Africa between 150,000 and 70,000 years ago. This serves only to emphasise the sapient paradox, for it increases the gap between the appearance of modern humans and the range of new behaviours associated with the agricultural revolution to something approaching one hundred thousand years."

It is now established that our species *Homo sapiens* migrated out of Africa about sixty to seventy thousand years ago, subsequently spreading to all the other continents. Recent observations suggest that the emigration was from the area of Africa now called Botswana. The first anatomically modern human remains were found in Africa and date from about 150,000 years ago. Before that, there was a period of time during which the new species *H. sapiens* grew out of the preceding species, now thought to be *H. erectus,* which itself had come from the preceding *H. ergaster.* This period of *speciation* was of course accompanied by changes to the human genome. It is apparent that changes also occurred through "cultural" influences in addition to the genetic changes. Human culture is learned after birth and can be learned from people who are not closely related genetically. This is known as co-evolution. The immediate predecessors of *H. sapiens* had much greater inquisitive and innovative natures than any other animals. They developed the controlled use of fire and other technological advances. These skills would have been passed on by demonstration and imitation and do not at all indicate the ability to speak language. The development took place mainly in Africa, in the African Middle Stone Age.

The observations made on the material record, obtained by archaeological investigations, can now be aligned with genetic observations. These are based on studies of mitochondrial DNA (mtDNA). Mitochondria are energy-producing organelles found in cell cytoplasm, outside the nucleus. The DNA within mitochondria is passed on in the female line (because only the egg contributes cytoplasmic components to the foetus) from generation to generation and is non-recombining and seems to be selectively neutral, therefore its molecular composition remains unchanged over many generations. Mutations in the mtDNA occur rarely but, it is thought, at a regular rate. They cause the DNA of the individual to differ in one place from that of their mother or sisters. After thousands of years, new lineages are produced and this can be used to trace changes in genome over time. The Y-chromosome in the male shows similar characteristics and has also been used to establish genetic inheritance changes over long periods of time. It is remarkable that these studies, which throw light on the genome of humans many thousands of years ago, are conducted on samples taken from people living now, or very recently.

To quote again from Lord Renfrew "The picture was summarised by the geneticist Peter Forster in 2004 in a clear and coherent way. On the basis of mtDNA analysis, it can be asserted that all living humans are closely related, and descended from ancestors living in Africa some two hundred thousand years ago."

"Studies of the mutation rates for mtDNA now permit an approximate chronology that ties in reasonably well with the radiometric dating available for fossil remains. It turns out that our species did indeed emerge in Africa and that the 'out-of-Africa' scenario is correct. The first and principal dispersal of humans ancestral to the living humans of today took place about sixty thousand years ago."

"It is clear now that the human groups outside Africa are all descended from what are called mtDNA haplogroups M and N."

"The implication here [from the DNA work] must be that the changes in human behaviour and life that have taken place since that time [the out-of-Africa dispersal], and all the behavioural diversity that has emerged—sedentism, cities, writing, warfare—are not in any way determined by the very limited genetic changes that, as we understand the matter, distinguish us from our ancestors of sixty thousand years ago. So the differences in human behaviour that we see now, when contrasted with the more limited range of behaviours then, are not to be explained by any inherent or emerging genetic differences."

Lord Renfrew wrote further "All this new information, this much clearer picture of the emergence of our species, soon leads us back to what was described earlier as the sapient paradox. If the genetic characteristics of our species, the human genome, emerged as many as 150,000 years ago in Africa, and if the humans who dispersed out of Africa some 60,000 years ago were closely similar to each other but also to ourselves in their genotype, why did it take such a long time before the emergence of those distinctly more modern behaviours that became apparent at the time of the agricultural revolution? It at once becomes clear that the take-off in human behaviour that we see, for instance, in the agricultural revolution was not linked with some DNA mutation, since the genotype had already been established for more than one hundred thousand years. If we are to understand and explain the major developments that we see in prehistory, it cannot be in terms simply of our genetic makeup, which had already taken shape one hundred thousand years earlier." These compelling statements by Lord Renfrew have all the academic authority to be accepted as correct.

Thus the genome of the humans who migrated out of Africa sixty thousand years ago was almost exactly the same as the genome of present-day people. All people living nowadays have an almost identical genome to one another and to the genome of sixty thousand years ago. There has been very little change except for the comparatively minor changes to skin colour and physique that characterise the different races of people seen today, which it is thought must have developed since the migration out of Africa. But of course there have been the most enormous changes in the behaviour, abilities and achievements of humans over these past sixty thousand years. Lord Renfrew calls this period the *tectonic* period, from the Greek word "tekton" meaning a carpenter or builder, indicating that it was a period of great change and development. It was due solely to cultural developments and not to genetic changes. It is a rather amazing thought that children born now have almost the same DNA as children born sixty thousand years ago. From the genetic aspect they have similar innate capacities. But these innate capacities remained hidden for many thousands of years, only starting to become apparent about ten thousand years ago. [Although it should also be stated that very small differences in the genome can have very large effects.] In other words, they had ability far beyond what they needed or what they used in their rather uncomplicated lives.

Lord Renfrew supposes that the difference between the child born sixty thousand years ago and the child born now is due to the different cultures that they are born into. That culture remained unchanged for about fifty thousand years until the sudden leap forwards of the agricultural revolution ten thousand years ago.

There seems to have been little response in the academic literature to answering the question posed by the sapient paradox. Something must have happened about ten thousand years ago that caused the sudden change to sedentism and the development of agriculture which led to the rapid development of more complex society. Lord Renfrew invites explanations from neuroscientists to account for the sapient paradox but the explanation will be through mental and behavioural change and therefore neuroscience may not have the ability to provide an explanation. It will lie within the provinces of theology and philosophy to provide an answer.

Later in the book Lord Renfrew describes the way in which human societies developed in different trajectories in different parts of the world. There is much information about the way society developed in complexity over the thousands of years of the tectonic period. But that is all past the critical moment when the hunter-gatherers suddenly decided to settle down into larger groups. Why did that happen ten thousand years ago and not twenty thousand years ago? Why did it happen at all, yet? It could have continued the same way for another hundred thousand years or another million years. After all, the horse has hardly changed over the past five million years.

Lord Renfrew says very little about possible causes for the sudden change to sedentism. He merely states "Most commentators, including Lewis Binford and Jacques Cauvin, accept that climatic change was crucial (global warming and the establishment of more stable conditions with fewer oscillations in temperature). This will have permitted a greater population density. Researchers such as Barbara Bender and Jacques Cauvin see social progress—meeting together for feasting or to conduct rituals—as key factors alongside the new ecological conditions."

Published attempts to answer the sapient paradox have not been notable. Some have tried to argue that the change was not as abrupt as supposed, pointing to some developments in tool making and art which occurred during the Speciation period, which ended about 60,000 years ago, before the start of the Tectonic period (10,000 years ago to the present). But these were small developments with little impact on the lives of the people, not nearly as significant as the great change from nomadic hunter-gatherers to the settled life of village dwelling agriculturalists. Another comment has been that the development of agriculture was prevented by adverse climate: the potential could not be realised because of the ice ages. The last ice-age ended about 12,000 years ago, but it would only have prevented agriculture in the northern areas; it would not have prevented the domestication of animals and plants in the temperate or tropical areas of the world. At the time of writing this book, there have not been any convincing scientific answers to either the sapient paradox or to the way in which our language suddenly appeared.

Lord Renfrew himself has discussed the sapient paradox in terms of seeking a neurological answer. He wrote "But the only conceivable solution to the sapient paradox requires that the performance of the human brain should be seen within a short-term evolutionary context where genomic change is probably not significant." Further, "…the neuroscience of embodied experience and of social engagement will be crucially relevant. For it is presumably on the basis of the neurological endowment of our species, present, even if still latent, within the human genome more than 60,000 years ago, that these emergent properties have been constructed." That is a perfectly reasonable view from a purely physical, scientific perspective.

But here we are dealing with behaviour, with properties of the mind and the spirit which are not physical. This moves the discussion beyond science into the realms of philosophy and theology. Scientifically, it seems that the human brain of 60,000 years ago had all the genetically endowed hardware that was needed to support the subsequent enormous advance in behaviour that occurred 50,000 years later. The emergent behaviour which characterises sedentism and agriculture must have been based on abilities in the brain which had been in place since the creation of people around 55,000 years earlier. The ability was there all that time, but was not stimulated until people began to attack each other and therefore needed to form larger groups for self-defence. Something suddenly happened to humans 60,000 years ago that introduced new abilities in the brain, especially for speech: the Language Acquisition Device proposed by Leon Chomsky. That occurred when God made people out of humans. God gave us the ability to talk to him and to each other. That is why we exist: to talk to God. This ability remained much the same until the behavioural changes that stimulated sedentism, namely the appearance of evil characterised by envy, greed and violence.

As mentioned elsewhere in this book it is unrealistic to expect that the methods of neuroscience can provide answers to this kind of question, just as dissection of a television receiver will not show the content of the broadcast programme. There must be certain neuronal pathways and signal conventions which constitute programmes in the brain, but it will be very difficult to decipher the programming language that the brain uses. There remains the enigma of how a person's thoughts, the most significant and meaningful part of their existence, relate to changes in electrical potential brought about by migration of ions through a membrane. And how that relates to their immortal soul. At present, it seems best for us to confess to complete ignorance about the answers to these questions.

The global warming referred to in a paragraph above took place in the Holocene climatic period which is taken to have started around twelve thousand years ago, with retreating glaciers. Then 11,400 years ago the Pre-Boreal period occurred, with a rapid rise in temperature over only about 50 years. Global warming continued during the ensuing Boreal period, up to around nine thousand years ago, with rising sea levels and the tundra of Northern Europe being replaced with forests. The brief Pre-Boreal period would appear to be the time at which there was a stimulus towards sedentism.

I believe that the more favourable climatic conditions enabled the hunter-gatherers to move camp less frequently. Instead of having to move on perhaps after a week, they were able to remain in one camp for several months because of the more prolific animal and plant life around them. That gave them the opportunity for some leisure for artistic or other non-essential activities: the making of spare tools, works of art and ornaments. For the first time, they were able to acquire more things—to acquire some wealth. This led to inequality which in turn led to temptation when a man saw, for the first time, that another man had more possessions than himself. That led on to crime: violent acquisitive crime. Once people were being attacked and robbed it became obvious that they needed to form larger social groups, for self-protection.

My explanation for the sapient paradox is fear. It was the sudden appearance of inequality followed by temptation, crime and violence which led to fear of each other and drove people to combine together in settled communities and to develop agricultural food production and a more complex social structure.

The Bible tells us that the first people, Adam and Eve, were able to talk to God. They knew only about what was good and were innocent and unashamed. They were made in the likeness of God. "And the Lord God said 'Let us make man in our image, and in our likeness will we make him.'" This indicates that the man of that time was to be modified, so that he would have the God-like ability to talk to God and to understand the meaning of goodness. He became 'a living soul'. These new people were distinct from the humans already living at that time, but their son, Cain, was able to marry and have children with one of the 'daughters of men', so they were the same species, biologically. The new people, who knew God, must have soon displaced the old humans. This is most likely to have happened at the time when the total human population had been reduced to very small numbers, which is thought to have happened about seventy thousand years ago.

At the end of the speciation stage there were *Homo sapiens* who had already acquired some technical skills in tool making and the controlled use of fire, but they were not people like us, even though they had a similar genome. It is thought that at about that time there were only a few thousand humans living. But this is by no means certain. The theory that the human population was decimated by the super volcano Toba, which erupted in Indonesia 74,000 years ago and caused massive climate change and destruction of life, is now being questioned as more information is being obtained about the layers of volcanic ash laid down. Genetic convergence studies using mtDNA suggest that there were only small numbers of people ancestral to ourselves. About 70,000 years ago there were probably only about 1000 to 10,000 humans living. The small numbers could have been due to other factors, such as epidemic disease. Perhaps that is why God acted at that point to give the humans a soul and language, to turn them into people and in that way avoid extinction because of their much greater efficiency. Then some of them migrated out of Africa and found territory that was more favourable to their survival.

When Adam and Eve were unable to resist the temptation of Satan, they became aware of evil. This was the sudden loss from their previous state, known as "The Fall". The Bible indicates that this happened soon after the creation of Adam and Eve. Adam did not "know Eve", that is, did not have sexual union with her, until after The Fall and the expulsion from the Garden of Eden. This suggests that it was very soon after the creation.

After that, Adam and Eve had children. They knew the concept of evil and that opened the possibility for violence as illustrated in the Bible by the murder of Abel by his brother Cain. But in my opinion this was a rare and special event. It was because Cain was jealous of his brother giving offerings to God which were more pleasing to God than his own. Generally, there was no temptation for the hunter-gatherers because they all had minimal possessions and there was no difference in wealth between them. Therefore they lived in peace and harmony with each other, in small family groups, praying to God and enjoying simple lives and the fruits of the earth. This continued for about fifty thousand years or more—such a long time compared with the five or six thousand years of the historical period. During this time they spread around Asia, Australasia and Europe and later to the Americas.

In this book, I propose that the answer to the sapient paradox is the introduction of a new form of fear, that is, people fearing each other. Until that time, humans had behaved like other animals, generally not harming other members of their own species, except for some fighting for sexual rewards, which was seldom fatal. Like other animals, they did not have knowledge of good and evil; they had no conscience. Then God made People from the Humans and soon after that the people disobeyed God. Then they knew good and evil and had a conscience, but they did not do evil until much later, when temptation entered their lives because they could see other people who had more than they had, and they wanted to take it for themselves. An important factor in the emergence of sinful behaviour would have been increasing language ability. This enabled a person to define and describe their frustrations and desires, and to discuss them with someone else, which might reinforce their feelings and their determination to take some violent action to get what they and their partner wanted.

Recent studies have suggested that there was little violence among the hunter-gatherers. Warfare could only begin when there were quite large centres of population, with a social structure in which leaders could decide to wage war, and had the ability to enforce their wishes on their subjects, or at least to gain their subjects' support.

Of course the ancient humans did have knowledge of fear. They were aware of the dangers of forest fires, floods and earthquakes. They were aware of the dangers from the animals living around them, and probably also of the dangers of poisonous plants. But they did not fear each other.

Once temptation and violence happened it must soon have become obvious that it was then necessary for people to band together into groups that were large enough to defend themselves. This would have been the imperative for the first villages, and of course once there was a village there had to be some form of agriculture to support the large population in one place. The hunting and gathering life style only worked for a small family group, in which case the hunters did not have to travel too far away from home to find enough prey and plants for their family. Once the group became large, perhaps a hundred families in one place, the distances to be travelled for the hunting and gathering of food became too great to be practical. Then it was necessary to increase the amount of food within easy reach, so the domestication of some plants and animals began. It was also necessary to develop some form of social structure so that people could live in harmony with each other and decisions could be made about matters of communal importance.

If there had been no knowledge of evil, no temptation and no crime, the development of village life might not have happened, or only very slowly, but the obvious need for protection hastened the processes of sedentism and urbanisation so that there was a dramatic change in behaviour over a period of only about one thousand years.

To clarify what is proposed here, the humans of sixty or seventy thousand years ago were given a soul and language by God. They became people overnight and could talk to each other and to God. They continued with a simple hunter-gatherer lifestyle because there was equality: nobody had more of anything than anyone else. Around 10,000 years ago some individuals began to acquire wealth, which introduced inequality for the first time. This rapidly led to violence and crime which stimulated the change to sedentism and village life to provide protection for the community.

That is my answer to the sapient paradox. It is of course a theological answer. It depends on belief in a powerful God who created one living creature who could talk to him. It is no use looking for scientific answers to this kind of event. It was a miraculous event that happened once only. That was how people were made, about sixty to seventy thousand years ago. The subsequent behaviour of people flowed from their minds and souls. They were happy to live at peace with one another as long as there was equality. Once some individuals began to acquire wealth, inequality became obvious and this led rapidly to strife. That is seen today, both within societies and within families. Inequality is one of the hardest burdens to carry without complaint. It does so often lead to hatred and conflict. So difficult for someone to accept that they have to live their lives with less than someone else. So that caused the conflict and fear which produced the start of sedentism and then agriculture about 10,000 years ago. This led to the development of more complex societies with increasing scientific and technical knowledge, escalating so enormously in the past hundred years.

11. Humans Evolved and God Made People from Them

In this final chapter, we will review the observations and suggestions from earlier chapters, and see how they can be fitted together to try to make some sort of reasonable conclusion about how humans turned into people, taking into account both scientific and theological aspects.

It is proposed that Humans evolved but that People were specially made. People were an upgrade of the human, improved by the addition of a soul and language. Both happened together, suddenly and recently, by the will of God and could not have happened without God, because the changes were spiritual, not physical.

The starting point has to be to reassert the difference between human beings and people. The hominid line diverged about seven million years ago and developed through a number of species, culminating in *Homo sapiens* about 150,000 years ago. These humans were clearly much more advanced than any animals. They had the ability to make tools that required a lot of skill and patience and they had the ability to make controlled use of fire. These attributes alone set them far above the other primates. They had much greater curiosity and creative ability. They were humans, but they were not people. The simplicity of their lives was not the determinant. What distinguished them from present day people was that they did not have a soul and they were without language and the accompanying intellect. In addition to language and the deep intellectual capacity that comes with it, people uniquely have an immortal soul which only God could have given to us, and this was done in quite recent times.

This change from a human to a person happened suddenly. The traditional idea of a steady development from monkey to man, illustrated by a series of drawings in which the monkey gradually became upright, is not true. It does not fit the material record revealed by archaeology. This record clearly shows a stepwise development from human to person. Other species show periods of development interspersed with periods of stability, but the sudden change from human to person is much more abrupt. There was a small but very significant step up for hominids when they began to make tools, and a further step up when they learnt how to control and use fire, but the very large step up occurred after humans were given a soul, language, intellect and immortality.

Thus the ascent of man can be seen to have taken place in four stages. Firstly there was the desire and determination to walk upright, which began about seven million years ago. This was followed by a long period of time during which there was a gradual development. We have little information about what pre-humans were like for most of this time, but we can recognise certain stepping stones along the way, from the fossils that have been identified. We recognise the life of Lucy, about three million years ago and Turkana Boy about 1.6 million years ago. Lucy and Turkana Boy were on the way to being human, but they were still animals.

The second stage began when a non-human hominid decided that flakes of flint were useful and they would try to make some more of them. That was the moment when one could say that they had become human (although not yet classified as Homo). They were no longer animals, because they had intellectual curiosity and creativity that is not seen in animals except in the simplest form. This development was reinforced later by the ability to make beautifully crafted hand axes and later still the controlled use of fire for warmth and for cooking, and for the manufacturing of pottery and metal objects. These then were humans of the genus Homo, with several proposed species leading to *Homo sapiens.*

The third stage was the transformation of the human *Homo sapiens* into the person *Homo sapiens.* (Linnaeus: *Homo sapiens var. sapiens.*) This was done at the moment when God gave humans a soul, immortality and language, together with the intellectual powers that come with the ability to use words to define and express complex ideas, including, crucially, the concepts of good and evil. This is likely to have been just before the migration out of Africa, about 70,000 years ago, as both those who left and those who remained became people. This was the Adam and Eve moment of the Bible.

Scholars now generally agree that some *Homo sapiens* migrated out of Africa, about 60,000 years ago. They were hunter-gatherers and it seems that they continued much the same life style as they had done previously, which did not differ much from those who remained in Africa. They were people, and lived as small bands of hunters and gatherers who led a mobile existence with no settled place to dwell. They lived in peace with God and each other, without envy or greed. They used a limited range of tools and had few other possessions, just what they could reasonably carry with them. They made use of fire and they were able to make stone-tipped arrows and to join with others to hunt in groups. They spread to people the earth: all people except the descendants of those who remained in Africa are descended from them.

The fourth stage was the great leap forwards that is seen so clearly in the material record, which shows the beginning of sedentism and agriculture about 10,000 years ago. Humans had become people about 60,000 years before that, at the time when there were only a very small number of humans living. Their great latent abilities remained largely unused during a long period of stability, while people enjoyed the simple hunter-gatherer life style. Then there was the sudden change to village life and domestication of plants and animals that Professor Lord Renfrew has described so clearly and called the *sapient paradox*: why was there such a long period of stability without change followed by a sudden and very marked advance only about ten millennia ago?

[It is very difficult to estimate the numbers of humans who were living a long time ago. It has been estimated that 200,000 years ago the effective hominid population size was probably about 10,000 to 30,000 individuals. At the time of the Toba disaster, 70,000 years ago, it may have fallen to about 1,000 to 10,000 individuals. Both are very small numbers. Contrast this with the number of foxes (*Vulpes vulpes*) that are thought to live in Britain at present—about 250,000 adults when at the lowest point, in the spring. Each spring about 400,000 cubs are born, with a very high death rate, mostly due to road traffic accidents. When Jesus was alive, 2,000 years ago the world population of people was probably about 300 million. By the year AD1800, the world population of people first reached one billion. The world population of people is now about seven billion.]

As Lord Renfrew explained in his book, one cannot look to genetic or evolutionary processes to explain the sudden and so recent change in people's behaviour. The genome of present-day people is almost the same as that of humans 60,000 years ago, or longer. Evolutionary changes take much greater periods of time to take effect and are not nearly as dramatic.

Lord Renfrew looks for answers from neuroscientists, but the sapient paradox is not a physical, scientific problem; it is a problem of behaviour, of the mind and the soul. All of us who believe in the soul have to accept that only God

219

could have given us our souls. It did not develop slowly bit by bit. A creature either has a soul or does not have one. But presumably there must be neurological pathways that enable the soul to connect to the brain and the mind. A kind of neuronal cradle that enables the soul to plug-in to the brain and mind. This could have developed slowly over a long period of time, but equally it might have happened in an instant. This is what neuroscientists might try to look for, but they are likely to have great difficulty in making progress. Understanding the relationship between soul, mind and brain is not only in the realm of the neuroscientists, but belongs probably more fruitfully with studies in philosophy and theology.

In previous chapters, it was concluded that the reason why people have our uniquely complex and expressive language is to enable us to talk to God and to each other, and that people were created when God gave us our souls. These two attributes, soul and language, are linked together and happened simultaneously. God made people in his "image and likeness", meaning that God gave us immortality and reason, which is dependent on language. Of course we are vastly inferior to God but the wonderful thing is that God has given us these attributes of immortality and language that were unique to God but are now shared by God with all people. Of course, some people do not believe this, they believe there is no God and no soul. This book is not for them, it is addressed to those people who do believe in God. It is for people who seek to understand how people came into existence under God's will.

The figure shows the time line of humans compared with the time line of higher mammals such as the horse and dog. The X-axis is marked off in millions of years ago, from now to minus seven million. The Y-axis is not calibrated but indicates development and increasing ability.

The lines are not strictly to any scale but serve to illustrate the qualitative difference between the human and animal. The two timelines are very different.

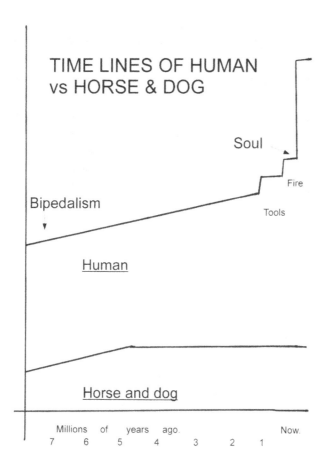

TIME LINES OF HUMAN
vs HORSE & DOG

Soul

Fire

Bipedalism

Tools

Human

Horse and dog

Millions of years ago.
7   6   5   4   3   2   1   Now.

Time lines. The human time line shows a steady development of ability from bipedalism, through Lucy and Turkana Boy to small step-ups due to the making of tools and controlled use of fire. But it was the introduction of the soul and language that gave the enormous uplift in ability that happened when the human became a person about 70,000 years ago. The change to sedentism and agriculture that took place about 10,000 years ago was a huge change in the way people behaved, but was not due to any change in their innate qualities.

Animals such as the horse and dog developed steadily over a long period of time and by about five million years ago had reached a certain stage of development which was evidently successful and did not need any further significant modification. They have remained essentially the same for the past five million years. The time line of the horse began about 58 million years ago

221

with an animal rather like a medium sized dog, named Eohippus. This became a larger more horse like animal by about 40 million years ago, named Mesohippus. By about 25 million years ago, this had become larger still and looked rather like a present-day Zebra, named Merychippus. By about 10 million years ago, this had become recognisable as a horse and was named Pliohippus. It remained hardly changed, to produce the various wild horses known today. This is a very long and very slow, gradual development which fits in with Darwinian Natural Selection very nicely. Development for 58 million years to produce a horse about five million years ago, which has not changed significantly since. Human development over the past seven million years has also been slow and gradual, up until the past 70,000 years, when the abrupt change from human to person took place. This is something so definite, so recent, so abrupt and so different to everything else that it cannot be ignored.

The start of the hominid/human line began about seven million years ago when it diverged from other primates with the beginning of bipedalism. These hominids developed slowly over a long period of time. Milestones along the route are Lucy (3 million years ago) and Turkana Boy (1.6 million years ago). This steady development continued at a very slow rate until small step-ups due to the advent of tool making and the controlled use of fire, which occurred within the last half million years. It was the supremely significant introduction of the soul and language about 70,000 years ago which marked the change from human to person. Sedentism and agriculture began only 10,000 years ago and was not accompanied by any change in people's innate qualities, but it was associated with understanding the concept of evil and fear of other people. That was why they had to cooperate in larger groups of settled communities. This led to all the ensuing technological advances.

Contrast that with the horse and dog who have remained virtually unchanged for the last five million years. It shows a completely different time line of development. Darwin's Natural Selection can be used to explain the first seven million years of human development, but not the last 100,000 years during which there was the sudden change from human to person. Darwin himself was not prepared to accept this and tried to show that people were no different to animals in evolutionary terms as discussed in the chapter *Descent of Man.* Wallace disagreed completely with Darwin over this. All people who believe that we have a soul have to reject the idea that people could have arisen by a physical process of Natural Selection, unaided by God, because only God could have given people a soul.

Looking again for a moment at the ancient fossils, how sure can we be that Lucy and Turkana Boy were really in the stream of organisms leading from primitive monkeys to humans? Both seem to be accepted by most paleoanthropologists but there are some dissenting voices, especially with regard to Lucy. Several hundred of her bone fragments were collected over quite a wide area and painstakingly pieced together in what seemed to be the right arrangement by their discoverers. They total about 40% of the complete Lucy skeleton. Perhaps this is not enough to be able to say too much about Lucy. However, there was no duplication of bone fragments, indicating that at least the fragments almost certainly came from the same individual. Ultimately, some more may be known about the true place of Lucy and Turkana Boy from studies of DNA and genetic calculations. It is already looking as though there is a large developmental gap between these two fossils. Lucy was named after the song by the Beatles called "Lucy in the sky with diamonds" which was popular at the time that the fossil was discovered, but this might suggest that Lucy was a human, which she most emphatically was not. Lucy was an animal. She lived about three million years ago, which is such a long time as to be impossible to imagine. It is fairly easy to think of a hundred and fifty years by reference to the lives of grand-parents or great-grandparents. It is just about possible to think of two thousand years, since the birth of Jesus Christ, by reference to historical milestones such as the Roman Empire, the Norman Conquest, the dissolution of the monasteries and the Napoleonic wars and World wars. But a million years is 998 thousand years longer than that. Lucy lived three million years ago: a very, very long time in the past.

Unfortunately some people cast doubt on Lucy being an ancestor of humans, for religious reasons. This is a mistaken approach. It does not really matter whether Lucy was one of our ancient ancestors or not: the fact is that there were millions of our ancient ancestors living over several million years, although we do not have their remains. We are here, we are physical beings, and we must have had ancestors. There is no point in anyone denying this, for whatever reason. Everyone should accept that humans evolved over millions of years: but *people* were made out of them by God, suddenly and quite recently. It is evident that God used a process of development from simple to more complex forms. It is therefore not reasonable to suppose that God would have created a person from nothing, "from the dust of the earth", when there was already a working human that simply needed to be improved upon. God had only to introduce a soul and language to the existing human. Upgrade the carburettor to fuel injection and the distributor to electronic ignition and you have a better car. People are an upgrade of humans. But what an upgrade! Rather like going from the Wright Brothers bi-plane to a supersonic aircraft. More than that because the upgrade from human to person introduced two completely new elements that were not present before. Previously there was no soul and no language. Suddenly there were both. Both soul and language are spiritual entities; they could only have been put into people by God, because God is the maker and ruler of the spiritual world.

In the first book of Genesis, it is written: "And God said, let us make man in our image and in our likeness we will make him." It does not say "Let us make a man." It was not producing a man from nothing. It was taking an existing man (and woman), and improving them by making them in the image and likeness of God by giving them a soul, language, intellect and immortality. Then they could talk to each other and to God and have the possibility of eternal life. These were God like qualities that previously did not exist on Earth. These were spiritual qualities which were not accompanied by any genetic change.

The man and woman (or women and men) that God upgraded were *Homo sapiens*. Cain was able to marry one of the "daughters of man" and to have children with her, who themselves had children, so they were evidently the same species. This at once demolishes the idea that Adam and Eve were the first humans. If they had been, there would have been no woman for Cain to marry. They were not the first humans but they were the first *people*. Once people had been made from the ancient humans the people would soon have replaced the older stock that had no soul and no language. The people were very much more advanced and efficient by virtue of their expressive language which enabled them to be much more communicative and to be able to share ideas and cooperate with one another. This was a sudden, single event which took place at some time in the last hundred thousand years, most likely about 70,000 years ago when there were few humans, just before the migration out of Africa. But it may have been that the idea of Adam and Eve given in Genesis was a simplification suitable for the understanding of the people of that time: that in fact *all* the people who were alive at the moment when God acted were given a soul and language simultaneously.

As explained in the Chapter "The *sapient paradox*", the change in behaviour from hunter-gatherer to sedentary agriculturalist which evidently took place about 10,000 years ago might have been stimulated by people suddenly becoming frightened of one another, because of some people becoming violent and aggressive. It is suggested that improving climatic conditions made living a little easier, with easier access to food, which gave people less need to move camp frequently and consequently more time for leisure and the acquisition of wealth. That led, for the first time, to inequality between individuals which gave the latent knowledge of evil the chance to assert itself and show itself in the form of envy, greed, aggression, theft and violence. During the time that all the people were equally short of possessions, there was nothing to steal, there was no envy and they lived peacefully together. Rather like University students living happily together while none of them have any money. It is only later, when differences in wealth emerge, that envy and associated acquisitive crime appear.

Another facilitator of sin/evil/bad behaviour was probably the further development of the range of the spoken language. God gave people a working language in an instant, but it was a simple language that just covered the essentials. As time went by, it became more elaborate, with the introduction of more words to define and describe objects and actions. Later on the ability to put abstract mental concepts into words would have developed and this will have supported evil ideas as well as good ones. Increasing individual wealth, leading to inequality, coupled with the increasing expressiveness of language, combined to produce the conditions that enabled the latent tendency towards evil to manifest itself. In addition, the inherited animal instincts of self-interest must have formed a background that promoted selfish actions. It was this mental state which led to violence, causing the sudden emergence of fear of each other that resulted in people combining together into village communities, clearly seen in the material record, together with the development of agriculture. This change to sedentism and agriculture was not a change in people, it was purely a change in the way people behaved.

This two-stage development of people fits the description given in Genesis. First God created Adam and Eve, giving them each language and an immortal soul. Soon after that they disobeyed God and became aware of evil. It is recorded that Cain committed the violent murder of his brother, Abel, but after that Genesis suggests that people settled down to living in harmony for some long time, until the conflicts between the Israelites and their neighbours, which took place several thousands' of years later. As with the creation narrative the time periods are compressed, but the order of events is clear. Both Genesis and the sapient paradox show the emergence of people followed by a long period of stability, suddenly changing very dramatically and recently, with the manifestation of evil at the time when sedentism and agriculture began, about 10,000 years ago.

The reason why people exist is for us to talk to God, to tell God what it is like to be a person with a physical body. A body that is subject to disease and decay, pain and hunger, pleasure and contentment. A dialogue with God about our everyday lives, our joy and sadness, our hopes and fears, and our worship of God for all his Power and Glory and for all his Love and Mercy. That is the only reason why we are here. It is hoped that the way in which God made us, outlined in this chapter, can be accepted by believers as a reasonable amalgamation of the scientific information that we have with the theological indications from the Bible and similar texts. Whatever further scientific information may become available in future, it will not give any insight into the reason for our existence. That can only be explained by God creating one living being who could talk to him.

Conclusions

Chapter 1

Science and theology are separate disciplines, and there is no conflict between them. They are separate ways of looking at the material world, and of thinking about God and the world of the spirit. The physical world and the laws of science were made by God.

Science uses observation, measurement and calculation. It makes use of experimentation and relies ultimately on mathematics.

Theology uses revelation, interpretation and faith. Experimentation is not possible and it makes no use of mathematics.

Science cannot detect God, just as a magnet cannot detect gold.

Atheists should not use science to try to disprove God because science is not relevant to the study of God. Atheists should keep only to theological arguments to support their beliefs.

Eminent theologians see similarities between the philosophical concepts which form the foundations of science and of theology, but that does not mean that science can be used to argue against God.

Critical realism is a common-sense way of looking at problems. It is being applied to theology, with the intention that theological propositions should be subjected to rigorous intellectual analysis, in the same way as scientific ones. But it is much more difficult to do this with theology because of the lack of observations and measurements. However, present day studies of cosmology and quantum mechanics are entering areas where observation and measurement are not always possible with the apparatus available today.

Natural theology argues that the complexity, precision, perfection and utility of the natural world suggest that it has been designed. Natural theology has been wrongly discounted by those who do not believe in God.

Intelligent design is a proposal at the molecular level which argues that there are very many irreducibly complex processes which could not have developed by a series of small steps, because only the complete cascade of biochemical reactions would provide a working system. A single living cell, which is the basic building block of all life, contains many such systems. So far there has been no convincing scientific explanation to account for the existence of irreducibly complex biochemical systems in living cells.

As science provides more and more information about the way the natural world functions, there are fewer places where there is no explanation. This is a cause for rejoicing and does not in any way reduce the role of God in the creation of the world. It just throws light on how it was done. However, many of the "explanations" are quite superficial. To fully understand a physical process it is necessary to understand the way in which molecules function, and that depends in turn on understanding the actions of atoms, based on the way in which their sub-units function. What makes a quark do what it does?

The Standard model of Particle Physics is understandable by very few people. Likewise cosmology is proposing ideas about the origin of the universe which most people would think impossible, but they are supported by mathematics.

Much of modern science is still controversial and undecided.

It is hard to define or understand reality. Philosophers believe that reality is stratified. Only 4.8% of the total mass/energy of the universe is made of baryonic matter. The rest is thought to be made of dark matter and dark energy which are not understood at present.

The great majority of people living today believe in God. Different religions have different ideas about the nature of God but relatively few people deny the existence of God. Disbelief in God is often due to the belief that there is no non-material or spiritual world.

Scientific writing is different to theological writing because scientific ideas can change as new observations and results are recorded, but the texts of religion are timeless and immutable.

Science deals only with the material world, which it seeks to understand by observation and experiment. Theology acknowledges the material world made by God, but has no interest in investigating how it functions. It is concerned with God and with the non-material world of the spirit, which is undetectable by science.

Evolution is concerned with the development of living forms from simple beginnings to the complexity and variety seen now. This has interested people for many centuries.

In recent times, it was Lamarck who first proposed a system of development based on the transmission of acquired characteristics. Later, Chambers proposed a system of development that was based on his observations but without specifying a mechanism. It was Charles Darwin and Arthur Russell Wallace who independently and simultaneously proposed that Natural Selection accounted for the development of living beings.

The Origin of Species is not about the origin of life: it is about the way species developed from pre-existing species.

Natural Selection depends on members of a species not being identical. They show differences, and the environment in which they live selects those that are best adapted to survive successfully in their habitat. When the variant characteristic is heritable, it may be preserved in later generations: beneficial changes tend to be retained but harmful changes are usually eliminated.

At the time of Darwin and Wallace, nothing was known about genetics. Darwin published a genetic theory of his own, Pangenesis, which was not correct. The science of genetics began with Gregor Mendel.

When Mendelian genetics became widely known, it was thought to be incompatible with Natural Selection and Darwin's ideas were discredited. Later Fisher and others showed that Natural Selection could operate within a framework of Mendelian genetics and Darwin's reputation was restored.

In the early years of the twentieth century, there was a lot of new information generated and a lot of controversy. The various ideas were brought together by Sir Julian Huxley in a book called "Evolution: the Modern Synthesis", published in 1942. This was a work of such scholarship and authority that it became accepted as the definitive account. It established the supremacy of Natural Selection over Variation as the driving force of evolution.

Eldredge and Gould published a paper in 1972, proposing that punctuated equilibrium is a better description of evolution than Darwin's gradualism, in many cases.

In the early years of the twenty-first century, there had been such great advances in genetics, genomics, evolutionary development and related subjects that further reappraisal was required. "Evolution: the Extended Synthesis" by

Piglucci and Muller was published in 2010. This gave great importance to non-genetic (epigenetic) inheritance and to the attributes of the developmental process within organisms as determinants of evolution.

It is difficult to evaluate the most recent work at this time. It may be some years before an agreed synthesis can be widely accepted. The subject is becoming more and more complex with the development of molecular biology.

Evolution has happened and is still happening, although the rate of change is usually too slow to be detectable until a long time has passed. There are many mechanisms involved. Natural Selection is only part of the story.

Darwin believed that Natural Selection accounted for all evolution, right up to and including modern people. Wallace thought that Natural Selection could only account for evolution up to *H. sapiens* but not including modern people. In this book, the opinion of Wallace is supported.

The minds of modern people are better than required so they did not arise by Natural Selection. No system of evolution based on only physical characteristics could produce people, because people have a spiritual soul which is not a physical entity.

Humans evolved and people were made from them, by God. Only God could have given people a soul, language, intellect and immortality. These are all within the spiritual realm. People only exist because God wanted to have one physical living creature that could talk to him and worship him.

Chapter 4

The human brain is large relative to body mass. It appears to have reached a stage of maximum efficiency and further increases in size are not likely. The large size of the brain does not account for the much greater cognitive power and intellectual ability of people compared with other life.

There is quite a wide variation in brain size between different people but there is no evidence that people with smaller brains are in any way less intelligent or less capable.

The processing power of a person's brain is probably only about three times that of a gorilla's brain.

It seems reasonable to propose that there must be software programmes in a person's brain that enable language and the higher intellectual powers, including conscience and worship.

A great deal is known about the structure of the brain and how it works. There is detailed knowledge about how nerve impulses are generated. But dissection of the brain does not demonstrate the thoughts that are being processed.

It is not known how migration of ions through a semi-permeable membrane can become thoughts.

Functional magnetic resonance imaging can show which areas of the brain are more active when certain mental activities are in progress but cannot demonstrate the words that are being used.

From the start of bipedalism, it was the greater brain *ability*, especially in terms of inquisitiveness, inventiveness, creativity and adaptability, which set the hominid line apart from all other animals.

Chapter 5

Charles Darwin published "The Descent of Man" in 1871. In this book he tried to show that his theory of Natural Selection could explain all of evolution, including the emergence of present-day people.

He did this by giving examples of the way in which the higher animals were similar to people in many behavioural characteristics. But similarity does not prove identity. There are important differences between people and animals which show that their development has not followed the same path. Darwin argued that people were essentially no different from the higher animals and had therefore evolved in exactly the same way, through the process of Natural Selection. This was disputed by Wallace and in this book.

There are some slight similarities in the behaviour of people and animals but they are insignificant compared with the differences. Absence of a soul and language in animals is of fundamental importance.

The soul of people and the language we use are unique. A child learns to speak by listening to its parents and others. The first people to speak had no one to learn from, they must have been taught to speak by God.

The modern tendency to equate people and animals has been very well countered by Raymond Tallis.

Animals are wonderful and they must all be treated with the greatest love and respect, but they are not the same as people. People are made in the image of God and have an immortal soul. Animals are completely innocent: they cannot do wrong. They do not understand the concepts of right and wrong. It is people who understand, but often make wrong choices and fall into sinful behaviour.

Cruelty or hardship to animals must always be condemned in the strongest terms. More needs to be done to reduce the abuse of animals worldwide.

Darwin thought that people had developed by a series of very small but equal steps over millions of years. He did not know about recent pre-history: that there had been a steady development for a long time, followed by quite recent step-like changes culminating in a sudden change in behaviour about ten thousand years ago, characterised by sedentism and agriculture. The change from human to person due to acquisition of soul and language took place about 70,000 years ago and was not accompanied by a change in the material record, they continued as hunter-gatherers for another 60,000 years.

Darwin was a Christian with faith in God, but he appeared to ignore the importance of the soul in defining people and making people absolutely distinct from animals. He also disregarded the great importance of language in defining people as distinct from animals.

Darwin believed that there was inheritance of acquired characteristics, which was not correct. He published his theory of Pangenesis which tried to explain this, but it had no factual foundation.

Darwin thought that our ideas about morality developed by a process of Natural Selection, simply because it was more efficient for a group of people if everyone showed consideration for each other. He thought that this removed the requirement for any special moral instruction by God but that did not change the fact that God must have created people.

There was a sudden change from human to person, unknown to Darwin, which took place in the last hundred thousand years. Believers will know that this must have happened because it is the only possible explanation which is consistent with the material record and with the spiritual world.

Part two

Chapter 6

God is everlasting so therefore is not a physical being, from which it follows that God must be a spiritual being and that there must be a spiritual world.

God has given people a soul and immortality, so we are spiritual as well as animal: animal bodies with a spiritual soul.

There must be an after-life for the soul, to maintain justice and to make sense of the complex and often harsh world in which we live.

We have no idea what the spiritual world, non-material world or "other" material world is like or what it is made of. But it must have some structure and rules of operation.

There is no proof of a spiritual world in the scientific sense, because science has no methods to detect the spiritual world, but there are a number of evidences which point to the existence of a spiritual world.

First of these is the almost universal belief in God.

Other evidences for a spiritual world are the activities of evil spirits. There is no doubt that they exist and show themselves at times. They can cause physical effects even though they are not physical. Once experienced they are not forgotten.

Psychic surgeons can perform amazing operations which cannot be explained by science.

People experience telepathy between close friends.

The way in which water can cause the powerful twisting of a wooden branch is evidence of an activity not currently understood by science.

The language that we all use all the time is a spiritual activity. Language does not have any physical basis: it consists only of ideas in our minds.

We use physical things such as ink and paper or computer screens to enable us to work with written words but the words themselves are spiritual. "In the beginning was the Word."

Words are spiritual entities which are the basic building blocks of everything. They were the first to exist, before anything else. "In the beginning was the *word*, and the word was with God, and the word *was* God."

Because we all use words we are evidently part of a spiritual world.

Disbelief in God is often due to people refusing to believe in anything that is not made of baryonic matter, but this is a restrictive view that does not fit the evidences given here.

Only 4.8% of the mass/energy of the Universe is made of baryonic matter.

To understand the totality of reality it is necessary to study science and theology at the same time, independently and concurrently, and to learn from both about the nature of the physical world and the nature of God and the spirit.

Chapter 7

People have a soul and a mind together with a body which has a brain.

The soul could not have been provided through a process dependent on Natural Selection because the soul is a spiritual entity, not physical, and Natural Selection is a physical process.

The soul is immortal.

Only people have a soul.

The soul probably develops in parallel with the body and mind and grows throughout the person's life.

The soul is the real person and forms a record of the person's life.

The relationships between the brain and the mind and soul are little understood.

Thoughts are supernatural entities. It is not known how migration of ions through a semi-permeable membrane can become a thought.

After death of the body, the soul continues to exist.

There are various ideas about what happens to the soul after death. It may sleep until the Day of Judgement or may go straight to Heaven or to Hell or to Purgatory.

Chapter 8

Language is an amazing attribute of people.

No other living creatures have language.

Communication with a few grunts does not constitute language.

Language is the language of Virgil, of Shakespeare, of Churchill and other great writers and orators of many cultures.

Language is of overwhelming importance to people.

Language enables people to talk to God and to each other.

The only reason for the existence of people is so that people can talk to God.

Generally people talk a lot, all the time, to express their ideas and to influence other people. Language is a very important part of most people's lives.

There is no agreement among scholars about when spoken language first appeared but evidence for written language only dates back about 6,500 years. It seems improbable that spoken language would have existed for a very long time before ways were found to represent the sounds with physical markings in clay, on stone, on wood and on papyrus as happened. Therefore it seems likely that spoken language cannot be from hundreds of thousands of years ago. In this book, it is proposed that spoken language began suddenly about 70,000 years ago.

Old theories about how language originated are laughable and of no value. More recent theories are not much better.

Ideas about how children are able to learn a language so quickly and easily are controversial, with nothing agreed at present.

Studies of language acquisition in children have little relevance to how language developed in the first place.

Studies of primates have no relevance to development of human language.

Leon Chomsky has proposed that a child has a Language Acquisition Device in their brain which gives them the rules of grammar and syntax that allows them to build sentences.

Modern theories about language development are too steeped in reverence to Natural Selection. There was no physical need for language. Other animals have managed perfectly well without it.

The need for language was to enable people to speak to God and it was God who gave people that ability.

A slow bit by bit development of language would not have worked. Language could only have started with a sudden, overnight, new ability given to a group of people living closely together, at the same time. People learn language from another person; the first people to speak must have learned from God.

Language is closely related to the soul because without language people would be unable to utilise a soul.

Language is essential to understand complex abstract concepts including belief in God and the meaning of good and evil, right and wrong.

The creation of people from humans probably took place about 70,000 years ago when there were very few people living and it was at that time that people were given a soul and language. This was just before the migration out of Africa. Their life-style as hunter-gatherers remained much the same for 60,000 years until the start of sedentism.

With the sudden change to sedentism and agriculture about 10,000 years ago, there was a rapid increase in vocabulary as people's lives and social interactions became more complex. The people were the same but their behaviour changed. They were the same people genetically, with a body and a soul, but they became more aware of evil at that time due to the development of inequality between individuals.

Chapter 9

The creation narrative given in Genesis is not completely in line with what science knows now, but is closer than the older or contemporary accounts, such as the idea that the world rested on the back of a giant turtle.

Genesis began as an oral tradition and was then written down over three thousand years ago. It is the word of God, but the word as given to and interpreted by the people at that time.

It had to be put in words and ideas that were understandable to the people of that time.

It should be seen as a simplified account of creation, as one might now explain something to a child.

Genesis is not a scientific book, but the closeness to reality in broad outline is remarkable considering its great antiquity.

It is therefore unreasonable to quibble about the use of "days" rather than "epochs". The ancient Hebrew word used in Genesis is "yom", which can signify either.

Creationists who take a very hard line on literal interpretation, and deny the geological evidence, do themselves no good and weaken the respect that should be given to the scriptures.

Belief in God should not depend too much on literal interpretation of ancient texts but upon a person's experience of God in their own lives and the world around them.

It needs to be remembered that the world began for people in the last 100,000 years. During that time there has been no noticeable evolution in the main groups of animals that we are familiar with, such as horses and wolves, or the main groups of plants such as oak trees and bracken. The world now looks the same as it did then, except for the devastation caused by over-exploitation of resources by a rapidly expanding human population. The human genome has hardly changed over the past 100,000 years.

Atheists have tried to use Darwin's Natural Selection to show that the natural world could have developed without God. Even if it **could** have it does not mean that the natural world **was** made without God. It would present two possibilities: with or without God. Believers are certain that God did make the spiritual and physical worlds and that God made people from humans.

If a designer made the world, it would look like Natural Selection because a designer tests their prototypes in the environment that they are intended to work in and eliminates the less fitted.

God made Heaven and Earth.

The Earth developed a wonderful spectrum of plants and animals by as yet imperfectly understood evolutionary and genetic processes.

God suddenly made people from the ancient *H. sapiens*, probably about 70,000 years ago just before the migration out of Africa.

God made people "In his own image and likeness", meaning that he gave them an immortal soul, language and intellect, making them the people that we are now, completely distinct from all other life.

We owe our existence to God: no amount of Natural Selection, working on primitive humans for however long, could have done that. Natural Selection is limited to physical matter and we are more than physical matter.

Chapter 10

The humans living in Africa 80,000 years ago were almost identical genetically to present day people. Some migrated out of Africa and spread around the world. They continued the same hunter-gatherer life style as before, living a nomadic existence in very small family groups with few possessions. This continued unchanged until about 10,000 years ago when there was a sudden change to sedentism and agriculture.

Lord Renfrew has posed the question "Why did they stay the same for such a long time, then suddenly change?" He has called this the *sapient paradox*.

The *sapient paradox* cannot be explained by evolutionary changes because the time available is too short nor by genetic changes because the genome is almost unchanged.

These are undeniable facts of the greatest importance.

There has been little academic response to this very important question.

It is clear now that the human groups outside Africa are all descended from what are called mtDNA haplogroups M and N.

The difference between the child born sixty thousand years ago and the child born now is due to the different cultures that they are born into.

The Holocene climatic period started around twelve thousand years ago. Then 11,400 years ago the Pre-Boreal period occurred, with a rapid rise in temperature over about only 50 years. Global warming continued during the ensuing Boreal period, up to around nine thousand years ago. The brief Pre-Boreal period would appear to be the time at which there was a stimulus towards sedentism.

It is proposed here that the more favourable climatic conditions enabled the hunter-gatherers to move camp less frequently because of the more prolific animal and plant life around them. That gave them the opportunity for some leisure and artistic or other non-essential activities, the making of spare tools and generally to acquire more things—to acquire some wealth.

This led to inequality which in turn led to temptation when a man saw, for the first time, that another man had more possessions than himself, and his wife will have seen it too. That then led to crime: violent acquisitive crime. Once people were being attacked and robbed it became obvious that they needed to form larger social groups, for self-protection.

My explanation for the sapient paradox is fear. It was the sudden appearance of inequality followed by temptation, crime and violence which led to fear of each other, which then drove people to combine together in settled communities, and to develop agricultural food production and a more complex social structure.

Of course this did not apply to all people and some societies retained the hunter-gatherer life style for thousands of years, some few remaining today in regions remote from much outside influence.

The humans of sixty or seventy thousand years ago were given a soul and language by God. They became people overnight and could talk to each other and to God.

They continued with a simple hunter-gatherer lifestyle without envy or violence because there was equality: nobody had more than anyone else. Around 10,000 years ago some individuals began to acquire wealth, which introduced inequality for the first time. This rapidly led to evil in the form of violence and crime which stimulated sedentism and village life for protection, as seen in the material record.

Chapter 11

It is proposed that Humans evolved but that People were specially made. This happened because it was God's will that there should be one living creature on Earth that could talk to him.

People were an upgrade of the human, improved by the addition of a soul and language. From this followed immortality and intellect.

Both happened by the will of God and could not have happened without God, because the changes were spiritual, not physical.

The first *Homo sapiens* of about 150,000 years ago were humans but they were not people. However well dressed and educated, if they could be alive today, they would not have been able to fit into our society. They were not people.

People were made by the addition of a soul and activity in the brain which enabled language. This probably happened just before the migration out of Africa when the human population was very small.

The people understood good and evil but led essentially good lives without temptation until they became tempted by the effects of inequality about 10,000 years ago.

There were four steps in the making of present-day people:

1. Bipedalism
2. Tool making
3. Controlled use of fire
4. Making people from humans: Soul and language, intellect and immortality. This led to a long period of prayer and peace for 60,000 years.

This was followed, about 10,000 years ago, by inequality leading to evil in the form of envy, fear and violence in some societies. This led inevitably to sedentism and agriculture in those societies, and after that to technology and warfare.

The time line for humans to people has a very different look from the time lines for other higher mammals such as the horse and the dog.

Horses and dogs developed slowly over many millions of years, and reached their present state about five million years ago. They have not changed significantly since then.

In contrast, the human line developed slowly for almost seven million years but then made some sudden changes in recent times. There were slight steps up associated with tool making and the controlled use of fire.

The enormous step up took place when humans were changed into people by acquisition of soul and language, about 70,000 years ago. Their behaviour did not change at that time, until about 10,000 years ago when for some groups of people envy, fear and violence led to village life and agriculture.

These very marked differences from everything else cannot be ignored.

Summary of conclusions

Life on earth has developed slowly over many millions of years.

The process of evolution is incompletely understood.

Darwin's theory of Natural Selection is only part of the explanation.

Scientific inquiry cannot be applied to God, the spiritual world and soul.

A long line of hominid ancestors which nominally began seven million years ago led to the latest species, *Homo sapiens*, about 150,000 years ago.

These were humans but not people. They became people when given a soul and language, intellect and immortality by God, probably about 70,000 years ago, before the migration out of Africa.

They retained a simple nomadic life of hunting and gathering and lived peacefully together until about 10,000 years ago. They could talk to each other and to God.

At that time, more favourable living conditions enabled some individuals to acquire wealth. This led to envy and violence in some societies, although some remained unchanged till influenced by other cultures much later.

The fear of other people necessitated the construction of larger communities for self-defence. That in turn made it necessary for people to increase their food supplies.

Sedentism led to agriculture with domestication of animals and selective breeding of some plants. All the subsequent development of people flowed naturally from these beginnings, leading to the development of larger more complex societies, technology and warfare.

Searching for a reason for our existence cannot be conducted by an appeal to science. Science attempts to explain how physical things happen but not why they happen. There is either no reason for our existence or we exist to satisfy a requirement of our Creator God. Nothing more can be said about "no reason" except to say that it is not true and if it were true it would be intellectually dissatisfying. We are here by the will of God.

Most people accept the reality of one God, who loves his creation. It was made by God to be loved by God. Although science has recently made wonderful advances in understanding how creation happened and how it then developed, there are two stages at which it seems that there probably had to be a special intervention by God: the start of the Universe and the creation of life. Much more recently there was definitely the change from human to person carried out by God about 70,000 years ago.

There can be no doubt that only God could have made a person from a human because of our soul and language.

Believers must reject the idea that people could exist without God. It is long overdue that the modern leaders of all Faiths assert that people could only have been made by God, who alone could have given us our soul and language, intellect and immortality.

No amount of any physical selective process could have done that. It is not reasonable to expect a scientific explanation for what is spiritual.

This does not mean any kind of rejection of science. Science is to be respected in its own sphere, but it cannot say anything about God, the soul and the world of the spirit.

Final Message

There is one God who recently made people in his image and likeness by giving *Homo sapiens* an immortal soul, after some millions of years of development. He gave us language and intellect so that we could talk to God and to each other. These are spiritual things, outside the reach of the physical sciences. They could not have come from a purely physical process such as Natural Selection. Only God could have done this.

The evolution of life over many millions of years is a complex process. Darwin's Natural Selection is a part of this process, but it is not the full explanation. Recent advances in the understanding of genetics and epigenetics are making many contributions, but there is not yet a full explanation of how life developed.

To be a complete person, it is necessary to talk to God, to love God with all your heart and mind and soul and strength, and to love all the people around you as much as you love yourself.